COPING WITH CRISIS: A WEST VIRGINIA DOCTOR'S PERSPECTIVE

Greenbrier Almond, MD

2020

International Standard Book Number 0-87012-921-X
Library of Congress Control Number 2020916688
Printed in the United States of America
Copyright © 2020 by Dr. Greenbrier Almond
Buckhannon, West Virginia
All Rights Reserved
2020

McClain Printing Company
Parsons, WV
www.mcclainprinting.com
2020

Front cover photo by Lois Flanagan Almond

Illustrations by Aliza Eloise Almond Pope, Emilia Sylvie Almond Pope, Harper Rose Landin Almond, Camille Ashmar Almond

DEDICATION

This is respectfully dedicated to Elizabeth Curry, my ninth grade English teacher, who gave me the assignment to write a term paper about the Passion Play of Oberammergau. This began a lifelong theme not only concerning the diagnosis and treatments of plagues and other diseases, but also being inspired by the Bavarian villagers' faith response, trusting God to spare them the ravages of the bubonic plague, which He did.

My heart's desire was to take my international family to Germany to witness the spectacular play, only performed every ten years. In 1990 when our children, Maria and Ronce, were close to my age when I learned much about plagues, my dream became a reality. Our pilgrimage set a pattern of belief for our children.

Now another plague—COVID 19—spreads across our world. My heart's desire now is to open the eyes of our granddaughters, Aliza, Harper Rose, Emilia and Camille, to emphatically know healing is the will of God. Jehovah-Rapha is His name.

The cover photograph is by my mother, Lois Flanagan Almond. It was taken from Mt. Nebo, Upshur County, West Virginia, highlighting the Coffindaffer Crosses strategically placed in the front yard of Mt. Nebo United Methodist Church. Stretching below and in the sunny distance is the "Promised Land Farm," of which my wife Araceli and I are stewards.

Bernard Coffindaffer, a Marine veteran and a native of Craigsville, West Virginia, was the man behind the crosses. He wished to remind people that Jesus was crucified on a cross at Calvary to forgive their sins and that He is coming back again.

ABOUT THE ARTISTS

When I began to apply myself 50 years ago to understanding what makes us tick, learning of psychiatry, I said to myself that this discipline is onto something profound. What intrigued me, then and now, is the subconscious mind—a data bank for everything which is not in the conscious mind. It stores the beliefs, the previous experiences, the memories, the skills. Everything that one has seen, done or thought is also there. And it is the guidance system.

Practicing psychiatric medicine provides opportunities to explore the subconscious mind. In evaluating children, I recognize they are not always able to verbally express themselves, so I ask them to draw a house, a tree and a person. This opens the mind wonderfully.

This book is about coping with crisis, particularly timely in the current coronavirus pandemic. Common to my previous books, this offering has illustrations from children. This time these children are our precious granddaughters. You will get a clearer image of the new norm—life with COVID-19 as a worldwide threat—from their art than from my words.

Aliza, age 8, clings to an art dream born two years ago in the Philippine Islands. She carries an inspired desire to be an architect engineer providing improved housing for Filipino children.

Harper Rose, age 8, loves all things art and music. She is blessed with perfect pitch and an ear for languages, already immersed in the French International School in Bethesda, Maryland. Her artistic rendering of Lola and Lolo captures our souls.

Emilia, age 6, crafts her art like her Lola and Lolo drew anatomy in medical school. Combine that with her apothecary skills—crushing her Lola's medicine and cleaning her cousin's wounds—and we see that she has the makings to be our next family healer.

Camille, age 4, gets top marks for drawing "anxiety"! Her life experience under attack is exactly what we are all living with from the threat of the invisible COVID-19 virus. One day Camille and Harper Rose enraged bees by throwing rocks at their nest. Panic ensued when the stinging creatures chased them. Dear Camille fell down, unable to escape. Fortunately our story ended well, as Mother Yasmine scooped down, rescuing Camille and earning the loving expression, "Mommy, you are my superhero!" Amazingly, all this is captured in Camille's art.

We are blessed indeed even in these trying times to see hope for the future from the creative minds of children.

(We also acknowledge the following websites from whom the girls garnered inspiration for their artwork: www.artforkidshub.com and youtube.com/DrawSoCute.)

CONTENTS

FOREWORD
by
Stan Frum

Greenbrier Almond, MD's name and title I first heard over 30 years ago. A young woman whom I attended church with was struggling spiritually which resulted in depression. She was referred to Dr. Almond, who lived in the same community of Buckhannon, West Virginia. Upon completion of a few appointments, she related to me how wonderful her treatment was with Dr. Almond. She was elated that he diagnosed her accurately and treated her with appropriate modalities.

Fast forward some 10 years later, I again heard his name when he became a new staff clinician at the Louis A. Johnson VA Medical Center. I was honored to serve at the same facility, as Chief of Public Affairs and Community Relations Service. It was not long after that I recognized that he had answered the noble calling to help veterans who were having difficulty in readjusting to civilian life. Dr. Almond was developing a recognized treatment program which was on the cutting edge of Post-Traumatic Stress Disorder, a fairly new diagnosis in the *Diagnostic and Statistical Manual of Mental Disorders*. He gained approval for his program with financial remuneration for the Medical Center to maintain the program. As anyone who has worked in a large bureaucracy can testify to, this was no easy task nor was it a quick one. Nevertheless, he persevered in his endeavor to have a recognized program throughout other VA Medical Centers within West Virginia and beyond its borders. It was quite a remarkable achievement and one which I know has helped countless veterans and achieved a higher degree of professional reputation at the Medical Center.

Greenbrier's reputation was soon secured in the veteran community as a professional clinician who cared about those whom he treated. This was not a sterile, cold, non-caring program environment. A treatment team was in place with various disciplines who also aided in Dr. Almond's endeavor. As a staff member in addition to being a combat-wounded veteran from Vietnam, it provided me with more insights into my own personal stresses, which I hid by becoming somewhat of a workaholic so I would not have to think about my overwhelming combat experiences and memories.

King James Bible Hosea 4:6 states, "My people are destroyed for lack of knowledge." The book which I hope you are about to read is truly the combination of Greenbrier's knowledge, wisdom, insight, experience, discernment and academic studies mixed with his keen awareness of how a person's spiritual condition impacts the natural state of their life and vice versa. It is my hope that if you are a clinician, a layman, a veteran, a member of clergy, a counselor, you will read the following pages that provide you a wealth of knowledge which transforms the lives of yourself and others.

I personally want to thank Dr. Greenbrier for taking the time to write down his thoughts on this important topic that can impart positive life changes for anyone who reads it.

ACKNOWLEDGMENTS

When the coronavirus pandemic gripped our lives in early 2020, I fell to my knees in prayer with my help meet, Araceli Ganan Almond, who urged we pray 2 Chronicles 7:14 (KJV): "If my people, which are called by my name, shall humble themselves, and pray, and seek my face, and turn from their wicked ways; then will I hear from heaven, and will forgive their sin, and will heal their land." We continue to grow deeper spiritually even as this invisible scourge devastates.

God began to make a way where there was no way that I could fathom. Certainly I acknowledge Ian Sneddon from Ireland, who sent a message urging me to pursue further sharing of our Post-Traumatic Stress Disorder educational video presentation we completed in 2006: "Hi Greenbrier. I am sitting here this morning watching a video of you—the PTSD program that we produced when I was working with MPL. The reason I am watching this is because I have had some thoughts about taking this a stage further that I would like to run by you and get your thoughts…Ian." This was the beginning seed of this book.

Major acknowledgments go to our four wonderful and artistically talented granddaughters—Aliza, Harper Rose, Emilia and Camille—who agreed to illustrate our book. My belief about children in general is that they are all geniuses in one way or another. I love the art they share. I love that Jesus said of children, "Suffer little children, and forbid them not, to come unto me: for of such is the kingdom of heaven" (Matthew 19:14 KJV).

Listening to the prompting of the Holy Spirit, I contacted Stan Frum, a Vietnam Veteran, Purple Heart and combat-decorated hero. I retired from service as Chief of Psychiatric Service and Medical Director of the Post-Traumatic Stress Disorder Rehabilitation Program at the Louis A. Johnson Veterans Affairs Medical Center 17 years ago. My request to

Stan was simple: "Write a foreword from your heart. Let the Lord lead you." He said yes, for which I am grateful.

Finally I offer a repeat acknowledgment that is ever before me—Holy Spirit inspiration. "Inspired" means "God-breathed" as well as breathing from the lungs physiologically. Since COVID-19 impacts breathing so much that respiratory machines can be required to sustain life, this is relevant. However, I can remember the moment of writing inspiration, tracing it to the exact time daughter Maria and daughter-in-law Yasmine announced their first pregnancies. Creativity began to flow through me.

How pleased I am to acknowledge the great editing skills of Kimberly Link Gilmore. Once again she has steered me wisely through the complex process of putting ideas down on paper to birthing a book. Her intelligent questioning has led to significant improvements in each volume, including the current book.

Greenbrier Almond, MD
07/31/2020

INTRODUCTION

OVERCOMER
May 6, 2020

"These things I have spoken to you, that in Me you may have peace. In the world you will have tribulation; but be of good cheer, I have overcome the world."

(John 16:33 NKJV)

Jesus summarizes in the 16th chapter of John's Gospel what will soon happen, declaring a wonderful victory. His statement applies to us who are challenged by living in the present age of a worldwide coronavirus pandemic, awaiting the second coming of Jesus Christ. No doubt about it, we certainly have plenty of tribulation this Spring of 2020. We can agree with that part of Jesus' statement no matter what else we believe. In our sufferings, even the stouthearted may find ourselves vacillating between despair and hope, doubt and faith. Jesus, addressing His disciples, did not require them to be dauntless in the face of adversity, but instead invited them to join Him in victory. Faith the size of a mustard seed may fail at times but can be joined or yoked to Jesus. Placing trust in God joins us to a triune Father-Son-Holy Spirit who is always faithful.

My wife, Araceli, was born and raised in the Philippines. Visiting family there many times over Araceli's and my nearly 45 years of marriage has opened my eyes to living on the edge. There is no safety net in the Philippine Islands for these dear folks whom we so love. By faith we were about to journey to our remote South Pacific Tablas Island this March 2020. Airline tickets were purchased. Bags were packed. Goodbyes were being said. We anticipated celebrating the fourth birthday of our precious granddaughter Camille on March 3rd, hugging all our wonderful granddaughters—Aliza, Harper Rose, Emilia and

Camille—before flying from Dulles International Airport near Washington, DC. But the background noise in the media indicated a growing health threat from a novel coronavirus spreading rapidly in China and beyond. We put a hold on our tickets out of caution. Was our faith wavering, or was God speaking to us, warning us "in this world you will have tribulation," this time as a plague?

Fast forward two months now to our shelter-in-place life, very cozy in small town Buckhannon, West Virginia, USA. Safe and secure from all alarms and harms, Araceli and I have immersed ourselves in writing a healing guide book based on years of clinical care to those suffering from post-traumatic stress disorder. We pray that the message will go out and be a practical lifesaving message.

Becoming an Eagle Scout included learning water safety. I learned the four basics steps to help: reach, throw, row and go:

1. REACH with whatever is available or at hand.

2. THROW a line, a buoy, a floating object to provide support.

3. ROW when the victim is further out, using a boat to save.

4. GO if the first three steps can't be used as a last resort swim to the victim.

This book is our attempt as senior persons to "reach" with clinical wisdom pearls and Jesus' words. We send the message with prayer for our world experiencing tribulation.

Prayers fill up our hours, granting us a peaceful time and a closer walk with Jesus. An example of our promptings came just today. Our custom is to greet our friends and family on their birthdays. During the nine years of our Total Life Clinic, we sent birthday cards in the mail to our 12,000 active patients. Mother Lois Flanagan Almond, whom we honor now in Heaven on this Mother's Day 2020, prayed over every card she addressed and mailed. The message in each card reflected our Total Life Mission following the

Great Physician Jesus: "I have come that they may have life, and that they may have it more abundantly." (John 10:10b NKJV).

Prompted by the Holy Spirit, we send greetings and prayer to our relative Fedelaida Balsimo Ganan in the Philippines, whose birthday is May 9, 2020. We send a Facebook message. Cousin "Geng" responds from the quarantined, locked-down metropolis of Metro Manila with its uncounted millions of citizens:

"For now we have tribulation! No money to buy even for the needs of the kids. We are hungry and there is a short supply of food: *Gutom at pagkakapos.*"

Reflecting on the desperate message, I have difficulty being of good cheer, but I do believe in the Overcomer!

Harper Rose Landin Almond, age 8

Emilia Sylvie Almond Pope, age 6

Post-Traumatic Stress Disorder
by Greenbrier Almond, MD

Presentation accredited by the American Academy of Family Physicians, 2006

(The following is a presentation I developed in 2006 on post-traumatic stress disorder. Although several years have passed, I believe there are potentially valuable insights that we can use today as we deal with the current coronavirus pandemic and its inevitable aftermath.)

Post-Traumatic Stress Disorder presentation by Greenbrier Almond, MD
Accredited by the American Academy of Family Physicians, 2006

This training course was developed to familiarize everyone with symptoms, treatments and services available relating to post-traumatic stress disorder, or PTSD. This presentation is designed to assist patients and counselors with the identification and treatment of the issues that can arise in a person's life, which not only affect the sufferer, but family members, friends and the sufferer's community. Your presenter, Dr. Greenbrier Almond, has several years of experience in treating and counseling veterans and other sufferers of PTSD. His kind, gentle manner will put you at ease as he guides you through the clinical and personal findings dealing with this disorder. He offers several helpful solutions and techniques that enable PTSD victims and their families to live fuller, happier lives.

**Rock-a-bye baby on the treetop.
When the wind blows, the cradle will rock.
When the bough breaks, the cradle will fall.
And down will come baby, cradle and all.**

Post-Traumatic Stress Disorder
We've heard this nursery rhyme all of our lives. There's a lot of truth in nursery rhymes. We know, for example, the wind

is blowing, it's always blowing. That is a figure of speech for the trauma, the stress, the life changes that are happening all the time. We also know that under enough pressure, a bough will break, and of course all may be lost when that happens.

What Makes an Experience Traumatic

This is going to be a discussion about how to deal with tragedy, how to deal with disaster, and remain in control. It's a study about the locus of control and what we can do to keep ourselves right when the wind is blowing. There are several things that we are going to talk about when we speak of locus of control. The first is: Why are some things more traumatic than others? Well, you can understand this first of all by knowing where you are on a continuum. There's internal control and external control. Something that is externally controlled would be outside of ourselves. That might be the weather. We really have no control over the weather. You don't like the weather around here? Just wait a while and it will change. And then of course there's internal control. Some things are inside of us, the very heart of who we are. And we're going to respond from our heart. For example, my heart goes out to children who have been abused and neglected. I have a tender spot for them. That would be something of my nature. I suppose I would even agree with the words of Christ, who said that if a child is harmed, it would be better that whoever harmed the child would have had a millstone tied around his neck and been thrown into the sea. That would be something from my heart. That's how we understand locus of control.

Hysteria

But also swirling around us in spite of real danger—and there's always real danger—are all sorts of things that heighten the danger. The news does this through fear, headlines, and hysteria—one of the things that Freud

3

studied. He was a neurologist who invented the treatment of mental illness by means of psychoanalysis. We think of panic. People have panicked about things that need not have been that severe. The run on the banks that happened in the Great Depression, for instance. We have overreaction. People understand what's happening, but they overreact. So these are some of the things we want to steer clear of as we guide ourselves in ways to handle stress.

Intentionality, Activity, Awareness
Another factor in all of this is that people are going to do things to us. This is the nature of the human beast. There are mean and nasty people out there. And we need, in the terms of the locus of control, to understand that some things may happen to us that are horrible but unintentional. Those would tend not to traumatize us as much. One example is this: Say a mother is caring for her child. In the process of changing the diaper, perhaps the mother accidentally pricks the baby with the pin, not severely but just a little bit. The baby will cry but is quick to forgive and is not traumatized by something like that. There are unintentional things that can happen. The intentional, though, can make us cringe and really affect us. Let us never forget the intentional evil that we saw in the Holocaust when millions were put to death. That's something that was very traumatic to the whole world at that time, and even to this day.

Level of activities is another way to think of this locus of control. Passive things sometimes happen, and we often are not as traumatized by them. However, if something is actively done to us, and the wind is really blowing, and it's not just blowing because of nature blowing it, but because someone has a wind machine, if you will, and they're actually trying to destroy us and the tree we are in, that would be more traumatic.

We also have different levels of awareness. Children are generally not aware of anyone's intention to harm them. And parents are always saying, "Be aware of strangers," but children are not aware. And as our level of awareness increases, we sometimes are able to avoid harm. But we need to know where we are on that locus of control.

The Biopsychosocial Model

Another way of looking at this occurred when Dr. George Engel first published his works on the biopsychosocial model. When you're trying to repair something that is broken, when there has been real harm, what are the ways to correct it? Well, the biopsychosocial model offers a perspective on that. We are, of course, our biology; we are the glands we have. The people that I deal with in particular with post-traumatic stress disorder often have a great deal of diabetes mellitus and glandular disorder, responding to stress that they had, often war stress. But we also are psychological. The word "psychological" or "psycho" has to do with the "soul." Someplace in us there is this understanding of what's wrong, the way things are to be, the way things could be, should be. You can think of all those types of ways of looking at it. Since the age of 12 most of us have understood certainly how things can be, and there is a psychology of who we are. That is something we can deal with in therapy. Another fact is that we are social people. We can never understand who we are unless we understand ourselves in relationship to another person. Take all that together, and you begin to understand the biopsychosocial worldview that is used in rehabilitation medicine today. When something's broken, it can often lead to some of the ways it is repaired.

Social Readjustment Rating Scale

The understanding about how we're going to deal with stress and define it first occurred during World War II. We were attacked as a nation under that horrible stress of Pearl Harbor, "a date that will live in infamy." And we had to go and fight the war in the Pacific. Speaking to two doctors, Dr. Holmes and Dr. Rahe, General MacArthur said something like this: "Give me only the healthiest recruits. We're going to island hop, it's going to be a long war, we don't know how we're going to do this. But we can't have people out there who are going to be getting sick. So I only want the healthiest." Dr. Holmes and Dr. Rahe realized that life change units, or stress points, have something to do with health. So their response was: "Let's devise a plan. We will say that if someone has suffered the worst stress there is, they've lost their spouse, then they're probably on their way to sickness and they probably will not be good soldiers."

As a starting point, they arbitrarily defined "death of a spouse" as 100 points on their "Social Readjustment Rating Scale." Then they begin to put in other life change units, such as divorce being 73 points. That's not quite the death of someone, but it is the death of a marriage. It is certainly a lot of life change. You can go on down the line. People who have had major personal injury or illness, they're suffering. That would be assigned 53 stress points. Looking at the preceding 12 months, a person adds up all their stress points. If they get over 135 points, they are subject to all sorts of minor illnesses. A lot of people are subject to these. If you go to a drugstore, just look at the over-the-counter section and see how many headache preparations there are. It will occupy more space than any other part of the over-the-counter section. That's due to people needing to take a medicine to handle probably about 135 stress points or life change units in their lives. People can get 160 points, 180 points, even more. These people are subject to major illness such as depression or anxiety, as we see in post-traumatic stress disorder, or such as physical manifestations like heart attack or stroke. We now know that when you take surveys of people who come to the ER with their first heart attack, you ask, "What were you doing four hours before the heart attack?" They'll say, more often than not, "I was in the fight of my life." They were in the midst of stress, and they built up a lot of stress.

The Most Common Responses to Trauma
Well, this is sort of a foundation, if you will, for dealing with "when the bough breaks." What are the most common responses to trauma? We know that the wind is going to blow and the cradle is going to rock, but we don't really have a handle yet on how we're going to respond to trauma. But we have choices. We can grow with what happens to us and grow out of it. Or we can spiral down, down, down into a depression. The choice really is ours, but we need to understand what we can do.

Growth of Control
First of all, any situation we arrive in, we have to understand what's happening. We become aware with all our senses: sight, hearing, smell, taste, touch. That helps us define our boundaries. A lot of people are losing touch with their boundaries in nature because they spend so much time indoors, and they are not as aware of what's happening. We don't raise our own food, we don't go out and exercise out-of-doors like we used to. But a foundation for health is to be aware, be aware of our surroundings and what's happening to us. And then out of that awareness we can gain understanding. We understand our limitations. I am a 56-year-old man. I cannot go out and run like I could when I was 19 years old and it seemed like the wind was beneath my feet and I could almost fly. But we have an understanding because of our awareness of what's happening to us. That places us in touch with reality.

After an understanding, we reach a decision about what we're going to do about what's happening to us. We make a decision, an effort to practice, to prepare for the future. So that's a spiral, and that spiral grows and gets bigger, and that's a healthy way. That's the way that children grow. A child learns more after they get their feet on the ground and they learn their language. They learn more in that one year from age four to five than a college student learns in four years. But there's a growth curve there, and it's quite remarkable.

Loss of Control
Or we can go the other way. We can spiral down. My father was an old country doctor who used to make house calls. One day he was called to a man's house, and it was a crisis. The wife said, "Doc, come quick because my husband is dying." Well, Dad got there to see that he had collapsed and probably was having a heart attack, and Dad began to do resuscitation efforts. Fortunately, Dad was able to bring the man back. The man said, "I was going down steps, I was going down toward heat and it was all dark." "Well," Dad said, "I'm not a theologian, but you'd better get to church next week." We can see there is a spiral down, and that would be towards destruction. We need to move toward growth.

Diagnostic Criteria for PTSD
Sometimes the way to understand health is to understand disease and what can go wrong. Since 1980 the American Psychiatric Association has defined this disorder we call post-traumatic stress disorder. First of all there's major exposure to something, an overwhelming trauma. And then the body and the mind and the psyche and soul, the very heart of the person, begin to try to make sense of what happened. Part of that is re-experiencing it. It is not uncommon for a PTSD patient to say to me that he lost his soul in Vietnam. Now a middle-to-late-aged man, he is re-experiencing the

trauma that he lived as a young man, 18 turning 19. He is re-experiencing that trauma all the time.

Sometimes there's avoidance, withdrawing from life, withdrawing from work. We had the Buffalo Creek Disaster here in West Virginia, and it prompted the study of people leading to the diagnosis of PTSD and its definition. There were people who were swept away, or their homes or loved ones were swept away, by the Pittston Coal Company dam bursting on that February day in 1972 at Buffalo Creek. Those people were never the same. They became avoidant. They never went back to work. They didn't keep themselves up. There were children who cried every time it rained. There were people who were never the same and became very avoidant and withdrawn.

Then of course the other response is hyperarousal, to become too alert and aware. We mentioned earlier that it can be healthy to be aware, but we can become hyper aware and aroused and can become very anxious. There's an old African-American spiritual "Nobody Knows the Trouble I've Seen." I heard a sermon referencing that and speaking about worry. We often worry about many things, but as the minister said, "Most of that never happens." We can prepare too much and worry too much and become hyperaroused.

Peters' Seven Steps to Radical Evil
Author Tim Peters in his book *Sin: Radical Evil in Soul and Society* looked at the steps people take from innocence leading to evil. He sought to understand why people are intentionally harmful to one another and why some people get caught up in doing harm and doing wrong, whether it's the Holocaust or Pol Pot in Cambodia, or whether it's some other horrible thing. We go through steps there, too. First of all, in our relationship to ourselves and others and to God our maker, we can see steps:

Anxiety: When people are getting out of step, they know that. I remember marching in the band in high school. We spent endless hours getting in step with each other. And it felt good when it happened. Whenever I was out of step, I felt anxious. I would be the first to notice that something was not right.

Unfaith: We can step down to unfaith. I remember a classmate of mine in medical school said he did not like to go to church because he was always feeling convicted. He was getting out of faith.

Pride: We can have pride. We maybe identify ourselves as better than others, and this takes us downward.

Concupiscence: We can have concupiscence, appetites that are hungering for things we should not have. This often has to do with lust.

Self-justification: And then we have self-justification, that somehow we are special, we are different, we deserve what we have.

Cruelty: Self-justification often leads to cruelty. When I deal with children who have been traumatized, one of the questions I ask the parents or ask the child is about how they treat animals. Some kids actually become cruel towards animals. Others only trust animals, and part of their way out is to allow them to, say, ride a horse, learning how to trust the horse. But cruelty can be part of this downward spiral.

Blasphemy: Then there's blasphemy, actually denying God and denying a person's very nature. So this puts us out of relationship with ourselves and others and God.

Pointman International Ministries
There was a group of soldiers that formed what is called Pointman International Ministries to help returning soldiers deal with PTSD. It was very clever that they took inspiration from the apostle Paul in the Bible. He did not go to southeast Asia, but he was in Asia Minor. And he writes in the way of someone with the wind blowing, and certainly he had

trauma. The bough nearly broke several times. He was stoned, he was shipwrecked, he was imprisoned. He writes on one occasion in Second Corinthians, "I think you ought to know, dear brothers, about the hard time we went through in Asia. We were really crushed, overwhelmed, and we figured we'd never live through it." (2 Corinthians 1:8 TLB). There's that word "overwhelmed" again. And he goes on to describe the doom and the uncertainty he was going through. But he found a Savior. As we go down through the scripture, Paul offers thanks and praise to God who upheld him, who was his anchor, who helped him not spiral downward but go upwards. There's a message in there for us.

Community
The other way that we're going to right ourselves or keep ourselves on the straight and narrow is through community. When we're feeling overwhelmed, we often can right ourselves by the community that we surround ourselves with. Wendell Berry, the Kentucky poet, wrote an essay about 17 sensible steps for community. As I reflected on it, I was reminded of the Amish who live in community. If you understand the Amish, they're not actually against modern equipment or progress in the sense of how to be better farmers and how to take care of the land. But what they are for is community. They will debate endlessly any new invention or new process. They are always deciding, "Will this build our community or harm our community?" We need to remember a sense of community.

John Wesley, when he was establishing the Methodist movement, had people gather together and ask each other every week in the sense of community, "How does it go with your soul?" If you go around a group of say 10 people and ask every week, "How does it go with your soul?" knowing somebody's going to ask you that, it's a way of repairing what's harmful, keeping us on the straight and narrow, and actually thriving in the midst of change.

Why These Responses Persist
When the wind blows and when the bough breaks, how are we going to deal with it? Why do we do some things that we do not want to do? Why do some things we do not want to see happen persist? Well, this is the question, and this goes back to that biological part of who we are.

Dr. Eric R. Kandel Wins the Nobel Prize
Dr. Eric R. Kandel of Columbia University in New York City is one of only two psychiatrists to have won the Nobel Prize for Medicine. He was awarded the prestigious honor in 2000 for his work on the nervous system cells of the sea slug. He showed that an animal or nervous system that is traumatized actually has changes in its biological makeup at the molecular level. I deal with veterans of combat and they tell me this. They say that when they returned from combat, their mother looked them in the eye and told them, "Son, you've changed. You're not the same person who went over there." And the person does feel entirely different.

When you analyze this from the biochemistry, the physiology, there are actual protein changes when an animal is put through trauma. So it is with the human nervous system. When you look at those molecular mechanisms, just as Engel postulated, you can go down into that cellular level and see there are actual changes that take place. One of the regions that enlarges in the middle of the brain is called the amygdala. It's an almond-shaped structure, and the name actually means "almond." A person suffering with post-traumatic stress disorder often has an enlarged amygdala. There are very real physical changes that take place. And that guarantees the persistence of some responses that we see with PTSD.

Erikson's Eight Stages of Development

Another factor in why things persist and how things hit us when the bough breaks is our age and in what stage of life we are. We owe a great deal of thanks to Dr. Erik Erikson, a Harvard professor who in the 1960s articulated the eight stages of life that we go through:

1. He said that we are most vulnerable in the first stage of our life, when we are establishing basic trust with that one person who means the most to us—our own mother. And on occasion for some reason there's a mistrust in that first year of life. And that sets the stage for paranoia, which is an absolute non-trust of anything, suspiciousness of everything. Paranoid people are miserable because they don't trust, and that can come from that first year of life developmentally.

2. Erikson looked at the second stage of life when children are gaining their autonomy. They are crawling around and recognizing who they are. If that goes well, they are on their way to discovery about everything in life. But some people learn to doubt their own ability even at that age.

3. The third stage of life is initiative. Freud was probably wrong when he said that there's a quiet stage from about age 6 to puberty. A lot of kids develop initiative then. They have projects such as 4-H projects, Scout projects, animals to feed, things to do. They develop initiative. But sometimes kids are faulted for that initiative. I've seen mothers shopping with their children. The child gets into the fray of things and wants to help shop. And then the mother will suddenly yell at the child and say, "Put that away!" because they are grabbing too many cereals or other items. The mother will grab the child and put them in the cart and say, "Just sit there." Guilt is instilled, and that sometimes harms a person beyond just the immediate moment. It's like the bough is breaking.

4. Then we have industry and inferiority, another stage of our growth. In the 1980s Dr. Richard DeVaul, a psychiatrist, was the Dean of the Medical School at West Virginia University. He was from Texas. He was sitting in Dr. Jake Huffman's living room here in our little hometown talking to doctors, and he said, "You know the difficulty here in West Virginia is that we have a sense of inferiority. I'm from Texas, and over there people have a sense of superiority." And it's true. If you look around, something has happened in these mountains, and we feel inferior rather than feel able. Maybe we lack something in the sense of industry. Not that we are not hard-working, but we have something to gain back that was taken away from us even at an early age.

5. Then we go into our adolescent years when we develop our boss self, our ego. And this is when many soldiers go to fight. They go off and they don't actually complete the developmental task. And so as I deal with people who suffer from post-traumatic stress disorder in their 50s, I notice an awful lot of adolescent jokes going around. There's a feeling that people are stuck back in the earlier phase of life. They have role diffusion; they never quite developed.

6. The sixth stage is young adulthood, and that is when we experience intimacy on a deep level. We have trouble understanding intimacy, don't we? Truly giving oneself to another person. Truly receiving from a person their love and intimacy. Since over half of marriages end in divorce, it's a problem, isn't it, intimacy? And thus this sets the stage for isolation.

7. Then going through the middle age, we want to see generativity. A major problem we face in our state is that one-fifth of the workforce in West Virginia are disabled. They're not generating anything, they're stagnant. And that's a big problem. Something has happened there. The bough

has broken, if you will. And the wind has blown, and we need to understand this and the persistence of it.

8. And then in late adulthood there should be integrity, which Erikson defines as the feeling of having contributed something to life. We hope we get to a stage where we have something to say about life to the next generation, and we don't just have despair and feel like we're giving up. And yet many older people commit suicide. You expect that person to have the feeling of integrity, but the heart is filled with despair. So there's a major persistence even into older age.

Distance from Target
What happens to us when we're traumatized? How does it persist, and why does it persist more often in certain times than others? Well, we have studies that examine this as well. How traumatic something is going to be can depend on how close it is to us. The closer the range, the more lasting the trauma:

*People who have been raped or have experienced sexual trauma are often the most harmed. There is of course the broken trust, especially when it involves a family member. But even more so, it's the sexual range, the up-close and personal range, that is most traumatizing.
*And then we have the knife range. People who fight hand-to-hand with knives are traumatized by being able to see the whites of the person's eyes. It makes it more traumatic to them.
*Next is the bayonet range. In Korea, the soldiers often fought with bayonets, and that was very traumatic. People came back with a higher rate of PTSD from fighting that way.
*Then we have the pistol range. People are traumatized when they can actually see whom they're killing and the fighting that goes forth.
*The hand grenade range is not as traumatic.

15

*The mid range, shooting with a rifle from a greater distance, is also not as traumatic.
*Further out we have long-range snipers.
*And finally, bombing from the air.

All these things are traumatic, but you can see the further the distance, the less the trauma. That's a factor in the persistence of that feeling of being overwhelmed in PTSD. These are war examples, but this is how the trauma often impacts us and our society.

Therapeutic Techniques

When the bough is breaking and that wind is blowing, what are we going to do about it? What are some helpful therapeutic techniques that will carry us through and help us not only survive but thrive?

There are things that make a difference. I had occasion several years ago to write an article about a patient and describe the techniques that I use in my own psychotherapy practice. I emphasize always that there's a positive power, and that's God. God is the foundation of everything. He's the ground of our being. We have a lot of things that overwhelm us, but still there's a God who understands, and as the creator, redeemer, and sustainer, is there for us. One time I worked with a man who was fond of saying, "I know there is a God, and I know that I am not He." And I think that puts it in perspective that we need to turn to that God, and that we can hide in the cleft of that rock.

The second thing is that we need to be searching for meaning always. I don't know that we will understand everything until the by and by, but we can search for meaning. Karl Menninger, one of the most famous psychiatrists in American history, wrote *Whatever Became of Sin?* In it he talks about our search for meaning and the need to reframe what is happening to us so that we can effectively deal with it.

Another area to consider is the area of trust. I mentioned that it's the foundation of our emotional growth, but when trust is broken, we can rebuild that trust. We do that through first being true to ourselves. When you are at the end of your rope, tie a knot and hang on. In our country we are fond of saying, "In God we trust." Every year I teach little Cub Scouts a project called "God and Me." I always get out a penny and show it to each child and ask them to identify what is written on our coin: "IN GOD WE TRUST." That's a beginning, a way to therapeutically deal with what is happening to us.

Then we have to deal with our anger. Anger is something that can eat us up if we don't deal with it. Depression is often defined as anger towards oneself. There are techniques we can use to deal with anger. For example, never letting the sun set on our anger is a way to deal with anger as it comes up in us every day.

Then we face our fear. A lot of times people are numb, and they are avoiding and in retreat. But if a person is going to gain control of their life, they are going to have to face the fear. I like the quote from the *Pogo* comic several years ago: "We have met the enemy and he is us." We have to face that fear.

We have to deal with guilt. Sometimes there are things that we have done that produce guilt. And it's only a matter of confession and understanding what it is that we've done and being responsible for our part in it. We can deal with that guilt. President Reagan used to go out to his ranch in California and cut filth. He'd do something physical, cutting and cutting. There are emotional issues that we can cut away, and we can turn things over to God again.

We have to allow time to work through things. Grief is a process, and we learn from Dr. Kübler-Ross and other early pioneers in grief therapy that working through grief can go on for several years. We can't hurry it up; it's not pathological. We have to allow it time to happen.

One of my favorite therapeutic techniques is setting aside a place of prayer. In understanding the life of Jesus, we recognize that he was a person of prayer and had a place of prayer. Often early in the morning he would climb up on a mountaintop and would pray. His disciples were impressed with that, and they said, "Teach us to pray." He was a person of prayer, and we can have a place of prayer. A lot can happen, more than we can ever know, through prayer.

Signs and Symptoms of Inner Peace

These are just techniques, and we can apply our own, and to our own broken boughs. And we can expect certain things to happen if we follow the process, if we trust the process. There will be signs of peace and tranquility that will well up in us. There is a list of "signs and symptoms of inner peace" that I've often looked at in my own need and shared with others. Allow me to touch on a few. The first is: "A tendency to think and act spontaneously rather than on fears based on past experience." Another is: "A loss of interest in conflict." I like this one in particular: "A loss of ability to worry. This is a very serious condition." Again, a lot of people worry and fret, and they're very obsessive about their worrying. I often ask my patients, "How long have you been worrying about this?" And they will often name some long period of time. But wouldn't it be wonderful to be able to say finally we have a sense of inner peace? Another sign is "Frequent attacks of smiling." People that smile most often have peace in their heart. All these are signs and symptoms that we want to have.

Rules of Being Human

Another way to look at all of this from a therapeutic standpoint and trying to work through what is traumatic to us, is coming to understand our human nature. We each have answers to life's problems that are going to be unique because we are unique. We need to ask, look, listen and trust. That's a very elemental beginning. The signs and symptoms of health are just like the signs along the roadway. Stop, look, listen. When people begin a therapeutic process, I always like to bring up the most powerful person on earth. I ask who that may be, and people name various people. The President of the United States is often named, and often the Pope is named. And I say, "What is the principal duty of that person?" And people reflect on that, think about, and understand that it's to listen. The President has many advisors, and the Pope has cardinals and bishops. They come and present and the person in that role listens. That's a very healing type of endeavor. And we need to allow ourselves time to reflect and listen. There are all sorts of ways we can consider ourselves human.

Defenses

Another thing that's important as a way to understand how we're going to deal with trauma as it comes our way is to realize that we have to defend ourselves. There's no way that we do not do that. Aesop's Fable "The North Wind and the Sun" has an important lesson. The North Wind and the Sun argue about which of them is stronger. They see a traveler and agree that whoever can make the traveler remove his coat is stronger. The North Wind blows fiercely, and of course the traveler pulls his coat tighter to keep out the cold. Then the Sun begins to shine, and the traveler at first loosens and then removes his coat because of the warmth. The lesson there is about the power of sunshine, of gentleness, and of love.

Narcissistic Defenses

We defend ourselves in various ways. Some ways work, and some ways do not work. For example, there are the narcissistic defenses. These are the defenses of people who are out of touch with reality; they are psychotic defenses. For example, if you deny something, that's not going to help you at all unless it's the common cold and will be over in 10 days anyway no matter what you do. But if it's cancer, you can't deny cancer. It's going to continue to grow, and it would be crazy to deny it. And sometimes a person will project. They may say, "I don't have any responsibility for anything. I project my responsibility onto other people. It's their fault that things are happening this way." That's nonsense. It doesn't take us anywhere in life. It doesn't help us. It's not a good defense.

Immature Defenses

We also have immature defenses. Certainly there are things that we do when we are young. When we are a child we think like a child, we act like a child, but then someday we grow up and we are no longer children. We should put away childish things. Kids know about the sick role, hypochondriasis for example. If you're sick, you don't have to go to school, you don't have to do your chores. You get to have extra attention from Mom. That's a powerful role. It's a defense, but it doesn't carry us very far. Your boss isn't going to be understanding if you don't show up for work for a long period of time. These are immature defenses. Another is acting out or showing off. They'll get attention, and they may distract themselves from what's important, but it won't get them very far toward health.

Neurotic Defenses

We have neurotic defenses. "Neurotic" simply means doing something again and again that's a failure, not learning from our mistakes. There are controlling people in this world. That is a neurotic defense. You can't control everyone. You can hardly control yourself, if you think about it. But when people are very controlling, that doesn't work very well.

We sexualize a lot in America. That's one small part of life, isn't it? Focusing so much on it is sort of a neurotic way to look at life. In terms of relationship, sex is important in a husband-and-wife relationship, but what about the other 23 hours a day? Or the other 23 hours and 40 minutes? In other words, there's more to life than that. It's a neurotic defense to focus on that.

Mature Defenses
We should be focusing on the sunshine, the mature defenses:

Altruism—to do something for another person who can never repay you. To help a starving child, to prepare a Christmas gift to send overseas to a child, something like that. That's a way to look at life that will improve everyone's life. It can solve a lot of problems in the long run, more than we will ever know. To be altruistic is a high endeavor.

Anticipation—we can certainly deal with life if we can anticipate what's down around the bend. We can plan ahead. That's a mature defense.

Asceticism—living a simple lifestyle, not going overboard materially. The concept can be seen in living on what I once heard as a "graduated tithe." As we are blessed in life, we give away more, always living simply.

Humor—certainly a mature defense. Will Rogers got us through the Great Depression as one of the most loved of all humorists. Humor is revered in our society. Bob Hope going to the troops with his Christmas program will always be remembered as one of the high points in our society, the

21

humor and laughter that he brought.

Sublimation—taking energy that we would give to something harmful and instead diverting that same amount of energy to something positive. There's all sorts of things that can happen if we don't care who gets credit for it. We can sublimate and supply ourselves. A person becoming a doctor, as I did, requires 12 years of school after high school. People ask, "How did you do that?" It's a sublimation, a looking ahead to helping other people who are sick. It's not thinking about studying 12 more years. There are different ways to look at life.

Suppression—we can in the heat of battle be wounded and not even feel pain until we're safe again, or until our buddy is also off the battlefield and is safe. Then we may realize we have suppressed the pain, and we can deal with it at that time. Those are defenses, the ways that we often deal with something traumatic.

Conclusion
You've probably identified with some of what I've said, and even realized that one short program like this is not enough and you might want to talk with someone. If that's the case, I hope you know that you're in good company. We as a nation were traumatized by 9/11 when our country was attacked and we saw the World Trade Center towers fall, and the Pentagon under attack, and the hijacking and crash of Flight 93. We were awed and were amazed at the strength and resiliency of our own nation as we went through this together. But you may be feeling left out. And if that's the case, and you feel that you need to have some more personal attention, I hope that you will turn to your family doctor, or to your minister or spiritual advisor, or to your local mental health professionals such as psychiatrists and counselors.

But whatever you do, don't just do nothing. This is a time of healing. We have come through a lot. They'll be some more traumas. These are wounds of a different kind. These are wounds inside of us. But they can heal and we can be stronger for that, just as a bone that is broken can heal and be a stronger bone and carry us on through life. You have a responsibility of course to your family. You may have children, a spouse, other people who care for you and want you to be strong and healthy. So whatever you do, let this be a beginning and part of the healing process for you and for all of us. And may that circle of healing and love cause you to be there for someone else when the wind is blowing in their life. Thank you for participating in this program, and please continue your walk of healing.

Harper Rose Landin Almond, age 8

Aliza Eloise Almond Pope, age 8

Personal Reflections While "Sheltering at Home"

Spring 2020

HUNKERING DOWN
March 19, 2020

Springtime in the mountains will be different in 2020 due to health authorities advising us to "hunker down" in place while we flatten the curve for infection by the coronavirus. My wife Araceli and I have enjoyed 44 springs together, each one being special in its own way. "Hunker down" is something my dear wife taught me early in our relationship. I recall a hike around Coonskin Park along the Elk River upstream from Charleston during which she suggested we take a rest. I had my way to rest, and she had her way. Being that we grew up on opposite sides of the world from each other, our customs differed considerably. I started looking for a log to sit upon, but she just plopped herself down on her haunches.

From Araceli's childhood she learned to squat. No need to have a chair or a log as she played on the expansive sandy beaches of Tablas Island, her South Pacific home. Araceli could make herself comfortable in a place or situation just by hunkering down. Now into our fifth year of living with her Progressive Supranuclear Palsy, I am grateful to God for giving my wife very strong quadriceps.

How perfect to be in training a lifetime exercising her quadriceps femoris, the group of muscles located in the front of the thigh. Though the signal from her brain to her "four-headed" muscles degenerates, Araceli can still arise from a fall gracefully due to her four mighty muscles: the vastus lateralis, vastus medialis, vastus intermedius, and rectus femoris.

However, United States President Donald J. Trump declared a national health emergency, not so that we could train our muscles by preparing to stay in a place or position for a long time, but rather to achieve preparation time and for our protection from this novel coronavirus. We are in the senior ranks now, so we are a high-risk couple for pneumonia or other complications, including death.

Yet, we have been training our souls for such a time as this. We have no fear of death. Our pastor from the Bible Center Church, Pastor Spradling, told us at our wedding ceremony in the chapel of EvUnBreth Acres in Buckhannon, West Virginia, on September 13, 1975: "Fear not." He reminded us that God's Word records a "fear not" for every day of the year. So has this admonition been true all our days up to now.

As we hunker down in our home, I have considerable time to read, to meditate, to pray and to observe my sweet "Honey Bun," my pet name for Araceli. She loves her siestas, again a custom learned in her parents' home. After lunch Araceli will rest about 45 minutes, as did her father, Judge Nemesio Ganan, Sr. Lately Araceli has been dreaming more, just as the Bible suggests happens to elders like us:

> In the last days, God says, I will pour out my Spirit on all people. Your sons and daughters will prophesy. Your young will see visions. Your elders will dream dreams.
>
> (Acts 2:17 CEB)

Now on this first day of spring, Araceli has a dream. She is breathing smoothly and even humming a simple tune of "Jesus Loves Me" in her sleep. Then with clarity not usual for her current speech fluency, she calls out: "Let us rise up and go!"

I find myself spontaneously calling over from my rocking-chair seat, "Where are we going?" only to realize she is still dreaming. Then down the back roads of my memory I am prompted to recall her same words in Coonskin Park after we had rested a bit.

For today we will hunker down, but soon and very soon we will be moving on our journey of life. My very spiritual life partner has an intuition that God has a new assignment.

She likens it to Moses being called at 80 years of age to lead the Israelites 40 years in the Wilderness toward the Promised Land. The name of our Almond Family farm in Hemlock, West Virginia, is "The Wilderness," and our farm downstream along the Middle Fork of the Tygart Valley River is called "The Promised Land."

From 4-H camping days I cherish songs that speak to my soul. Now I sing:

> I'm gonna sing when the Spirit says sing...
> I'm gonna move when the Spirit says move...
> And obey the Spirit of the Lord.

FINISHING THE COURSE
April 4, 2020

American English is a difficult language to master. Really, with singular focus I still struggle. My wife speaks six languages, including American English. Araceli writes poetry and sings American Jazz to perfection, indicating the degree of mastery she possesses. At this time of the coronavirus pandemic, we have spent quality time on our sunny porch analyzing the entirety of the concept of the word "course." We feel the imperative to do so. Perhaps we are finishing our course. Saint Paul's final chapter of his final letter has the statement: "I have fought a good fight, I have finished my course, I have kept the faith" (2 Timothy 4:7 KJV).

Of course, we ponder.

The apostle Paul, shortly before his death, wrote to his protégé Timothy. He writes of life as a race and declares that he has run well enough to receive a prize: "Now there is in store for me the crown of righteousness, which the Lord, the righteous Judge, will award to me on that day" (2 Timothy 4:8 NIV). Having run cross country at Buckhannon-Upshur High School, I appreciate his image. For example, when finishing 12 years of service as Chief of Psychiatry at the Louis A. Johnson Veterans Affairs Medical Center, I described the experience as "a great run!" That included hiring eight psychiatrists and the teams involved in four grants for our major diseases of substance abuse and post-traumatic stress disorder. We passed all our Joint Commission examinations every four years. And I developed a recreation program that was recognized as the best in the VA system for small hospitals. Another highlight was developing a hospice program while serving as Chair of the Ethics Committee. Serving on the Veterans Integrated Service Network Finance Committee helped me grow assured at managing a billion dollar budget.

31

"Course" can also be a part of a meal, Araceli reminds me. While enjoying a cruise in the Mediterranean Sea, we had one of our most extravagant dining experiences. Our captain was an author as Araceli and I are authors. When he discovered this, he invited us to a Captain's Dinner with eight courses. We talked about writing and reading and challenges in life. Then the captain, his wife, Araceli, and I simultaneously realized we were living life of incredible significance, yet looking forward and never losing sight of the true life ahead. A full course meal for sure.

As we ponder other uses of the word "course," Araceli and I remember our trip across the mountains with our children Maria and Ronce to visit Thomas Jefferson's Monticello. "When in the course of human events, it becomes necessary for one people to dissolve the political bands which have connected them with another, and to assume among the powers of the earth the separate and equal station to which the laws of nature and of nature's God entitle them, a decent respect to the opinions of mankind requires that they should declare the causes which impel them to the separation," wrote Thomas Jefferson in the Declaration of Independence. We felt drawn to this great man and his home. There we discovered more about the "course of human events."

Through her study of the Bible, when the children were very young Araceli discovered Psalm 112:

> 1 Praise ye the Lord. Blessed is the man that feareth the Lord, that delighteth greatly in his commandments.
> 2 His seed shall be mighty upon earth: the generation of the upright shall be blessed.
> 3 Wealth and riches shall be in his house: and his righteousness endureth for ever.
> (Psalm 112:1-3 KJV)

She instilled this "mighty upon earth" idea into our children's young hearts and minds. I believe the Spiritual seed has birthed an amazing drive, impelling Maria through Harvard Medical School into her gifted healing role as a psychiatrist. Ronce has recently achieved his current position as attorney serving the United States Commerce Committee. Both are becoming mighty in the land. They may think they are forging their own course in life, but there are times when God's markers become evident and they see they are following God's course.

As we two lovebirds sit in the sun on our expansive front porch, we reach out our hands to each other, grasping tightly. Gently I look into her wide eyes and recite Robert Browning: "Grow old along with me! The best is yet to be." I pray God's blessings be on us as we finish our course.

OBERAMMERGAU PASSION PLAY
April 7, 2020

Great teachers transform lives. Elizabeth Curry was such a teacher, for she ignited a spark in my life in 1963 when she asked me to do a Freshman English term paper on the Passion Play of Oberammergau. Even now in 2020 during Holy Week, once more celebrating the Passion of Jesus Christ, I am on fire living out a transformation Teacher Curry ignited. We are in the midst of 181-nation, worldwide plague pandemic. I am sheltering in place just as the Bavarian village did during the bubonic plague in 1633.

Following their pledge to God to spare their village the death that killed one in four in Europe at that time, I pray in pledge to God to spare our Appalachian mountain village of Buckhannon as potentially millions worldwide face death from the coronavirus pandemic. I extend my prayer for protection not only here but to a passover for the homes of our children in Farmville, Virginia, and Bethesda, Maryland, and the sparing of death for the homes of our families and friends around the whole earth.

The performance of the drama portraying the Passion of Christ every ten years forever is what those mountain folk promised centuries ago. I pledge our talents and energy to tell the old, old story of Jesus and His Love daily as long as I have breath.

Following Elizabeth Curry, I want to uphold public education as the principle tool for getting out the life-transforming message. Perhaps Mrs. Curry faced persecution for assigning a spiritual topic to a 9th grader at a public school. After all, the United States Supreme Court decided the case of Engel v. Vitale in 1962, in essence declaring official prayer in public schools unconstitutional. Certainly Elizabeth Curry knew this landmark United States Supreme Court case would make her courageous assignment suspect. From my perspective Mrs. Curry was saying, "Here

I stand!" Incidentally, the director of the current rendition of the Passion Play has selected two Muslim villagers to play key roles. The director and the actors are making a "Here I stand!" statement. These pledges to God continue to transform.

What my term paper meant for me as an American teenager was a statement that I would seek to grow spiritually as well as in body and in mind. That drive took me through the projects of 4-H, including my "charting" project the next summer. I mapped my life including serving as a 4-H Camp Big Chief for many moons all over West Virginia, inspiring four-fold development based on Jesus' life: "And Jesus increased in wisdom and stature, and in favour with God and man" (Luke 2:52 KJV).

Later as Araceli and I raised our own family, I realized a lifelong dream inspired by Teacher Curry. Unabashedly I "knew that I knew that I knew" that our family must go to Europe in the Summer of 1990 to the Bavarian village of Oberammergau and experience the Passion of Christ play. For after making the pledge, the village chose on every decade to spend a year setting aside other mundane tasks to act out the drama, involving the entire village from old people to children to farm animals.

I must get there, I determined. The Holy Bible records: "For the Lord GOD will help me; therefore shall I not be confounded: therefore have I set my face like a flint, and I know that I shall not be ashamed" (Isaiah 50:7 KJV).

And we made it! It was truly perfect in timing for 13-year-old Maria and 12-year-old Ronce. We fell in love not only with Oberammergau but also with Neuschwanstein Castle (the inspiration for Walt Disney's Cinderella Castle), the Rhine River Cruise, Switzerland, Paris and other locations in France, the highest glacier in Europe, and much more. How wonderfully transforming for our international family.

Now here Araceli and I are hunkered down in our home during this Passion Celebration 2020 as yet another pandemic threatens human life with disease and death. The villagers of Oberammergau were spared from the bubonic plague when they prayed to God, pledging their time, talent and resources. Certainly the choice I make is the one Elizabeth Curry put me on the path to make. When I walk through the valley of the shadow of death, I will pray every step of the way to a God who keeps His promise.

"THE FOOT ON THE ACCELERATOR"
April 11, 2020

Slogans define our lives.

"Remember the Alamo" reminds us of the Battle of the Alamo, so pivotal an event in the Texas Revolution.

"A day that will live in infamy" reminds us of the attack on Pearl Harbor on December 7, 1941.

"Let's roll" reminds us of Todd Beamer's call to the GTE operator and the heroism on Flight 93 on 9/11.

"That's the reason why we need to keep, as I say, putting the foot on the accelerator and not the brake," reminds Dr. Anthony Fauci, MD, director of the National Institute of Allergy and Infectious Diseases since 1984. The good doctor was appointed by Reagan and has served continuously under every President for 36 years, including President Donald Trump. Dr. Fauci first joined the National Institute of Health in 1968 and has been pivotal in US efforts contending with viral diseases like HIV, SARS, the 2009 swine flu pandemic, MERS, Ebola and COVID-19. President George W. Bush awarded him both the National Medal of Science (2005) and the Presidential Medal of Freedom (2008).

Dr. Fauci continues to be a pivotal medical leader who has inspired many of us during the coronavirus quarantine period to maintain shelter in place and social distancing as we flatten the curve of our horrific pandemic.

His slogan will be how many of us remember COVID-19, which is like no other event in the history of the world, equivalent to a war that effectively has shut down 184 nations' economies and infected millions. Homo sapiens versus coronavirus has left us with a primal tool—human behavior. The war is fought as hand-to-hand (hand washing) combat with safe social distancing and sheltering in place as the best hope for saving millions of human lives.

Our family stays in touch through social media FaceTime and Zoom technology. We share personal stories that encourage us. How amazing to see our resiliency as this plague ravages the daily scheduled lives we formerly led as a matter of course. Our son, Ronce, has a poignant tale of his oldest daughter from their Bethesda, Maryland, home:

> Harper Rose and I were riding bikes on Thursday evening. As we pedaled home, I asked her what she thought of the coronavirus. I wondered if she was scared given the constant news, or discomforted by the upending of our daily routines. She replied: "I am glad the coronavirus is allowing us to share so much time as a family." Innocent and beautiful, like a spring bloom. Even as this crisis has caused much pain, fear, and uncertainty, the virus has forced the world to stand still, to shelter in place, to leap down from its spinning axis. And from this new position we may see anew. So even as it is a time of pain and death, it is also a time of re-discovery and rebirth. Easter indeed.

At this Easter time when we all want to get back to normal, let us also remember that the first Easter was at Passover. It commemorated God sparing Israel from another plague of death. Jewish families huddled together in their homes to share a meal and memories, spared from the plague by the blood on their door and their faith that God was with them. Yes, Passover was our Jewish spiritual ancestors trusting God. They worshiped at home and spent time counting their blessings and naming them one by one.

Our daughter, Maria, called to offer Easter greetings, too. She had just heard a retelling of a parable that she first heard from me. Apropos to the hell that many are going through, including persons infected by the coronavirus, their family and friends, as well as first responders and health care providers in the war zone:

A person dies and is knocking at the Pearly Gates of Heaven to see if he can enter. Saint Peter checks the book of life. He finds the person's name and opens Heaven's gate.

Saint Peter welcomes the person to join a banquet in progress. The tables are spread with exquisite food served on golden platters. The hall is filled with laughter from the diners. The music is from heavenly choirs of angels.

The odd feature noted by the new arrival is that the serving utensils are very long, but the solution is readily apparent—each person is serving a partner across the table, so all are eating joyfully.

Just before he joins the party, he pauses and turns to Saint Peter. He has a request: "How wonderful to be in Heaven for eternity, but may I have just a glimpse of Hell?"

"Of course," Saint Peter says, taking him by the hand to go down to Hell. How strange upon arrival in Hell to see the same banqueting table with the same lavish spread.

"Saint Peter, this is not what I expected," the person declares. "Just as much food!"

"Yes," notes Saint Peter. "However, look closer and you will see that every starving resident is angry and in turmoil. They, too, have overly long utensils. No matter how they try to twist and bend, posturing selfishly, they cannot get any food into their own mouths!"

Maria and I appreciate the familiar tale of Heaven and Hell. We immediately understand the application. Social and physical distancing is not only for the person sheltering in place, but also for the good of the neighbor who may be older or suffering with chronic illness. For that neighbor, the coronavirus infection may be a fatal illness.

A final reflection on slogans comes back to one we use often in our shared mountaineer life: "We are all in this together!"

HEALING TO THE BONES
April 15, 2020

Gracious words are a honeycomb, sweet to the soul and healing to the bones.

(Proverbs 16:2 NIV)

Mom felt things in her bones, to hear her tell about it. Frankly, as a young boy or even to the time of her death when I was only 48 years old, I did not comprehend a need to heal the bones in the way she expressed it. Yes, there were my three broken bones in the second, fifth and seventh grades, but Doctor Dad took care of those with plaster of paris casts in six weeks.

Now with a heap of living and some further pondering on the Proverbs, I have gained a bit of insight. Mom is now talking to me from the past. I can see the weariness in her face and the sadness in her voice as my deep well of memory draws up a draught.

Araceli and I continue to shelter in place as the coronavirus traumatically alters our world: over 2,000,000 infections and more than 129,000 deaths so far as of today (April 15, 2020). The tsunami continues. I am weary. I need healing in my bones.

Knowing that we are body, mind, and soul, Araceli and I seek healing in our bones in all ways. We boost our immune systems by eating more fresh fruit, including bananas, pineapples, grapes, oranges, and apples. We exercise by stretching, lifting, and walking, remembering again Mom declaring that as she kept up our home she got as much exercise as if she walked eleven miles from Buckhannon to the French Creek Game Farm. We sleep, "early to bed and early to rise" as Benjamin Franklin advised in *Poor Richard's Almanac*.

To keep our minds healthy, we meditate on God's promises on many topics sweet for our souls—healing, hope, humility, and more. Especially we claim the promises dealing with fear, such as...

> So do not fear, for I am with you;
>   do not be dismayed, for I am your God.
> I will strengthen you and help you;
>   I will uphold you with my righteous right hand.
>   (Isaiah 41:10 NIV)

I remember Mom rising early in our hilltop home. I would join her in our kitchen where she would be reading God's Word. She told me she was partial to Isaiah in the Old Testament and Romans in the New Testament. So I go down memory lane with her to these secret garden spots.

Seeking healing in the bones, Araceli and I look for gracious words to be our honeycomb. My dear "Honey Bun," as I fondly call her, brings to mind the comfort her father gained by singing his favorite song, "What a Friend We Have in Jesus"! He told us that as Mayor of San Andres, Romblon Province, Philippines, he was confined during World War II. Separated, he grew fearful not only for his life to be spared but also for the health and safety of his wife and children, including baby Araceli. There imprisoned he began to sing...

> What a friend we have in Jesus,
> All our sins and griefs to bear!
> What a privilege to carry
> Everything to God in prayer!
> Oh, what peace we often forfeit,
> Oh, what needless pain we bear.
> All because we do not carry
> Everything to God in prayer!
>
> Have we trials and temptations?
> Is there trouble anywhere?

We should never be discouraged;
Take it to the Lord in prayer.
Can we find a friend so faithful
Who will all our sorrows share?
Jesus knows our every weakness;
Take it to the Lord in prayer.

Just for today, we dose ourselves with gracious words that are sweet honeycomb to our souls and healing to our bones. Further along tomorrow, we will seek additional health and wholeness. We live abundantly in the here and now.

BEING ALONE DURING ISOLATION
April 16, 2020

A West Virginia University School of Medicine grand rounds during my 1970-1974 student years shaped my future perspective on health care like none other. The premise of this particular presentation was that isolation is unhealthy in so many ways. Believing this to be true in my own life, having been blessed with a wholesome and loving nuclear family, I have wanted the same for my patients over the past 50 years. When I took specialty training, I emphasized Family Therapy in my WVU residency in Behavioral Medicine and Psychiatry. Also, I stretched myself to stay active in Family Medicine, even becoming President of the West Virginia Chapter of the American Academy of Family Practice. Over the years I followed psychologist James Dobson's *Focus on the Family*, even writing for his magazine. Attempting to stay current for continuing medical education, I earned a Fellowship status in Family Medicine.

We are now in the midst of a 30-day shelter-in-place order given by our governor, following the advice of our leading public health doctors as we mitigate the horrible coronavirus pandemic. I am forced to face the experience of isolation for myself. Here is an illustration of a lesson learned from a Facebook post I saw recently:

> To everyone struggling with being
> alone during isolation…
> This is how our grandmas and grandpas
> and parents feel when we don't visit.
> This is how the older people in
> nursing homes feel when no one visits.
> Remember them when this is over!

My faith teaches togetherness, too. Perhaps the deepest human need is a need for safety, safety in connection. We are social creatures. We are:

*Created by a Trinitarian God: "Let us make man in our image..." (Genesis 1:26 KJV).

*Told that it is not good to be alone: "It is not good that the man should be alone..." (Genesis 2:18).

*Born into an earthly family that is intended to reflect God the Father's heart: "For this cause I bow my knees unto the Father of our Lord Jesus Christ, of whom the whole family in heaven and earth is named..." (Ephesians 3:14,15).

*Reborn into the body of Christ where each one of us is a vital part: "Now ye are the body of Christ, and members in particular." (1 Corinthians 12:27).

Beginning at a ripe age of 64 years, I became a grandfather. Truly this is the crowning glory of my senior years. Thank you Aliza, Harper Rose, Emilia, and Camille! Experience and neuroscience come together to confirm that we are social creatures. From infancy we are hardwired to connect emotionally. Babies recognize their mother's voice from the womb, and an attachment is already forming. Babies are born looking for faces and from 1 to 2 days of age can imitate facial expressions. Attachment Theory research validates the connection between parent and child as essential to health and the foundation of safety for the child. Without this connection, the child's nervous system develops less robustly. Children are not able to regulate themselves; they need a healthy, present, attentive person. That is why I teach the granddaughters all those funny 4-H camp songs, and why I am so delighted when they respond as Camille did in Australia, frequently singing "E-I-E-I-O"!

THE RACE
April 17, 2020

"There is an old saying that the course of civilization is a race between catastrophe and education. In a democracy such as ours, we must make sure that education wins the race." —John F. Kennedy

The race is on. I am in the running. Even in my wildest dreams I probably could not have imagined what has become the new norm following the coronavirus pandemic.

Yes, our brilliant daughter wrote papers as a study-abroad college student at Oxford University in Great Britain where she understood a coming chaos. That was nearly 20 years ago. I pondered about her intuitive warning then, but nothing earth-shattering happened and the globe kept spinning. Obviously as a Wellesley College English major, Maria saw something more than I could see from the top of an Appalachian mountain in West Virginia.

I walked along several forest trails pondering her papers, including reflections on the dreadful thought "...the centre cannot hold..." from one of Yeats's poems:

> Turning and turning in the widening gyre
> The falcon cannot hear the falconer;
> Things fall apart; the centre cannot hold;
> Mere anarchy is loosed upon the world,
> The blood-dimmed tide is loosed, and everywhere
> The ceremony of innocence is drowned;
> The best lack all conviction, while the worst
> Are full of passionate intensity...
> —William Butler Yeats, "The Second Coming"

Certainly Maria followed the thinking of John F. Kennedy seeing a race between chaos and education. She sprinted ahead, gaining educationally by matriculating at

Harvard Medical School and earning an MD. Then she topped the crest at Duke University entering a challenging residency in Psychiatry. That might be a nod toward chaos, too. Certainly mastering Public Health at the University of North Carolina prepared her foremost for our first-ever medical emergency declaration in all 50 states that we are in the midst of now.

Not to be denied, chaos runs strong. Can the center hold? Will this very contagious and virulent virus infect Araceli and me, as well as the 20% of West Virginians who are elderly with serious co-morbid conditions? Sheltering in place becomes our only option.

But it is not a passive state of life. I tend to model my life after people I admire, like Clint Eastwood. Recently I read a story about the 88-year-old that inspired me. Singer Toby Keith asked Clint Eastwood how he keeps going, having just begun work as director and actor in the film *The Mule* at that time. Eastwood answered, "I just get up every morning and go out. And I don't let the old man in." And that then inspired Keith to pen the song "Don't Let the Old Man In."

Araceli and I are both medical doctors educated to fight disease. Words of wisdom come to mind from Dr. Harold D. Almond, my dad, words he shared the day I graduated from medical school at West Virginia University. He observed that at that moment in time I knew more factual knowledge concerning disease pathology, microbiology, and pharmacology than I would ever know again, but in 50 years I would be a better healer. Coached back into the race by Dad's words: Never give up! Keep on running! Keep my eyes on a mark past the finish line!

Catastrophe and education are running this course that determines civilization's survival. Education can still win the day. That is why I ran for the Upshur County Board of Education ten years ago and still serve, seeking the best way to achieve our mission statement: "To provide academic preparation; social responsibility; employability; and a desire for lifelong learning" for our students!

That is why the proceeds from our books go toward 529 educational savings accounts for the four granddaughters' higher education! That is why we underwrite the Nemesio and Maria Villanueva Ganan Memorial Library on Tablas Island, Philippines! And that is why I spend my time upon awakening each morning seeking spiritual truth in the Good Book!

SOOTHSAYER
April 18, 2020

Knowing that I am walking down an uncharted path with Araceli, my life partner, during this time of coronavirus pandemic under shelter-in-place orders, I have decided to journal every day. Just like Hansel and Gretel in the fairy tale who are taken into the deep forest, I want to be cautious about finding my way home. How clever the children were collecting pebbles and marking their trail lest they lost their way, unable to find the way home.

Our son Ronce journals, too. He has a sharp learning curve in his new position as Counsel for the Senate Commerce Committee. As he finds his way, he collects pebbles that define his duties. "Soothsayer" is one small pebble, he shares with us. To fully understand what our creative son means, I went to the dictionary. "Soothsayer" is commonly defined as one who predicts or foretells the future. The word "sooth" is an archaic word for "truth." So literally, a soothsayer would be someone who "says the truth."

Now I can wrap my head around the concept of soothsayer by applying the principle to the practice of medicine in the West Virginia hills. We "Docs" manage patients' life emergencies. A patient is someone who suffers. Our stock and trade is to examine, make a diagnosis, prescribe a treatment and come up with a prognosis. The prognosis part is also our soothsayer part. Folks want to know how much suffering they will have and for how long! West Virginia doctors are good at defining the misery load our patients will carry.

Here I go full circle back to my childhood, hearing this story about medieval Germany from my Scots-Irish parents, then telling it to my Filipino-American son who picks up Hansel and Gretel as a subconscious and creative way to solve the Senate Commerce piece of the path forward through the coronavirus pandemic.

I ponder the similarities. These medieval German children known to the Brothers Grimm are struggling/suffering in their shelter-in-place home of their poor woodcutter father. When a famine settles over the land, the woodcutter's wife (their stepmother) decides to take the children into the woods. Her plan is to leave them there to fend for themselves, so that she and her husband do not starve to death.

I share with Ronce the soothsayer my lesson learned from the Hansel and Gretel fairy tale: Do not to trust strangers, even if they treat you well. Be careful in commerce to make good deals. Be wise like Hansel collecting pebbles and leaving a trail to find your way back out from the deep forest that is the coronavirus pandemic.

IN CHRIST EASY YOKE
April 20, 2020

Dr. Marcia A. Bohn Khalil, MD, a mature Christian West Virginia physician and a friend from our years of medical education together at West Virginia University School of Medicine, signs her annual Christmas letters, "In Christ Easy Yoke." Coming from her deep and abiding walk with Jesus, Araceli and I appreciate her reference to how she is living out her years. We rather believe she is using code to tell us that doctoring in the hills has some rough patches, but her partner in practice is the Great Physician, so everything is alright.

During these tumultuous days sheltering in place because of the coronavirus pandemic, we have decided to get the rest of the story for the catchy sign-off "In Christ Easy Yoke." Here are the words of our Lord and Savior:

> Come to me, all you who are weary and burdened, and I will give you rest. Take my yoke upon you and learn from me, for I am gentle and humble in heart, and you will find rest for your souls.
> (Matthew 11:28-30 NIV)

Scratching my head sometimes stirs up my remembering, I tell Araceli. Today I searched through the back roads of my memory for references to "yoke." Soon I recollect from growing up on the hill above Buckhannon, West Virginia. There my memory roots grew deeply and fondly. Certainly my best childhood playmate ever was Danny Daniel. I cannot recall a time when we were not friends. Nor can I recall a time we did not accomplish our goals, which often ended up being creative projects like making stuff that involved carpentry. This is where his dad, "Big Dan," really helped us, for he was a master carpenter. And "Little Dan's" maternal uncles—the Long Brothers—

51

and his dad built our hilltop home as well as the Daniel residence.

Naturally good spirited, Big Dan would agree to help us when we outlined for him our ideas. He would cock his head as he looked at our rough sketches and then say in his deep Southern drawl, "Yes, that will be easy." He told us Bible stories including the fact that Jesus' earthly father, Joseph, was a carpenter. For 30 years Jesus was known as a carpenter's son, and then as a carpenter himself. I do believe carpenters like to say things are easy—certainly Big Dan and Jesus are in agreement!

One of those endless summer days in our childhood, Danny and I met after chores were done to play at whatever our hearts desired. My chore on this particular day was to weed a strawberry patch. Certainly it seemed like an "upon my word, a long row to hoe" day after we commiserated with farmer Lena Stansberry, a wonderful farmer neighbor widowed at a young age, who nevertheless held onto the family farm.

Soon Danny and I had a bright idea. We could get help in the future from our faithful companion dogs. Danny's rabbit beagle and my sheep dog collie could be harnessed up in a yoke so they could pull a plow through the strawberry patch, saving me work as well as allowing us more play time.

Danny liked the idea. He liked my ideas and I liked his. We had a mutual admiration society going. A yoke would be doable. We headed out for the Daniel lean-to barn to search for scrap lumber that we could shape into a first-class yoke like we saw in the Methodist Sunday School pictures. Danny attended Central Methodist Church, and I attended First United Methodist Church. The remembered poster showed father Joseph and young boy Jesus in their Nazareth Carpentry Shop making an oxen yoke.

Soon we were explaining our project to Big Dan, who scratched his chin as he studied our rough blueprint and then our board. "We need to make a trip up country to Gaines, where at the Long Family Farm we will find a more suitable board," he proclaimed.

Soon enough we boys and our dogs were bouncing along country roads leaving a trail of dust. Upon arrival, we all took a break for freshly squeezed lemonade and freshly baked cookies in the breezy farm kitchen. Over treats we heard that the crawdads were on the move in the creek. Well, that certainly would be worth checking out.

So faithful dogs and faithful friends holding newly acquired coffee cans in hand ran for the creek. Indeed, this was the World Series day of catches. There were more than enough for us to start a crawdad farm using the spring that flowed out of the hill between the Stansberry Farm and the Daniel Farm.

Boy, were we excited.

Later on Big Dan asked us if we wanted to pick out a hardwood beam for our proposed yoke. He said the oxen yokes in the Holy Land were approximately 50 to 80 inches long and about 6 to 10 inches across/deep, but our dog yoke could be smaller. He estimated it would take us a week or two of hard work to carve out the yoke.

Danny and I looked at each other and then at our coffee cans of crawdads. Together we studied the board and then shook our heads "no"; we had a new project playing in the spring to create a home for our crawdads.

Uncertainty abounds today in the face of the worldwide coronavirus pandemic, yet I am comforted by my memories from the gentle days of boyhood, heartfelt and free in Christ's easy yoke.

HONEST TO GOD
April 25, 2020

Sheltering in place gives me the opportunity of a lifetime to experience the cloistered lifestyle of a monk. As a youth I considered such a life of devotion, living in a garden, experiencing a deeper walk with God. Now a second chance. Do I give thanks to God or to the COVID-19 plague for such a pause?

Knowing the transformative camp experience of my early adolescence, I started down the cloistered way when I directed 4-H camps, science camps, poverty camps for underprivileged kids, and church camps and retreats all over West Virginia through college and the first year of medical school. Those times were so comforting, as our week-long camps enclosed us in from the outside world—a separated walk but not alone. The campers, staff and I benefited from that seclusion where the sharp laser-like focus of purposeful living allowed our light to shine and our imaginations to fly free and high ecstatically. Definitely sheltering in camp helped my healthy growth—growing in body, mind and spirit.

But this coronavirus pandemic quarantine has a desperate quality. Certainly high anxiety, if not panic, grips the world. What those in authority offer appears insufficient. This is a dark place and a dark time. Death lurks. An invisible virus invades with all the stealth of an enemy. My need for God is sharply felt.

"Nearer, my God, to Thee," I sing as I quiet myself, seeking God in my here-and-now human condition as I sit quietly by our fireplace watching the sparks fly upward.

Then I remember the troubles of Job:

> Yet man is born unto trouble, as the sparks fly upward.

(Job 5:7 KJV)

Then God enters my dark place:

> My tears have been my meat day and night, while they continually say unto me, Where is thy God?
>
> (Psalm 42:3 KJV)

Sheltering in place these 30+ days allows me to gain insight and to grow in faith as I hear His Words. My God reminds me of better days:

> When I remember these things, I pour out my soul in me: for I had gone with the multitude, I went with them to the house of God, with the voice of joy and praise, with a multitude that kept holyday.
>
> (Psalm 42:4)

I am aware of God's unfailing goodness in a truly blessed life. I recall prayerfully setting goals and reaching them: earning Eagle Scout rank; studying medicine and practicing the healing arts these 50 years; marrying up with Araceli and growing an international family together; living long enough to share "joie de vivre" with four precious granddaughters, and so much more.

God challenges me to remember that He has walked with me every step I take:

> Why art thou cast down, O my soul? and why art thou disquieted in me? hope thou in God: for I shall yet praise him for the help of his countenance.
>
> (Psalm 42:5)

On March 13, 2020, United States President Donald Trump declared an emergency for COVID-19 under Sections 201 and 301 of the National Emergencies Act. West Virginia State Governor Jim Justice's State of Emergency followed on March 16, 2020. From then, Araceli and I have cloistered ourselves.

It only took a spark from the Bible. Now we feel the warmth of God's lovingkindness as followers of the Way. While we cloister we seek answers to questions that still linger:

> Yet the LORD will command his lovingkindness in the daytime, and in the night his song shall be with me, and my prayer unto the God of my life. I will say unto God my rock, Why hast thou forgotten me? why go I mourning because of the oppression of the enemy?
>
> (Psalm 42:8-9)

Now I understand why a Sabbath rest is required of us. Now I know why we sing "Farther Along" in our country churches, knowing our day of full understanding is not yet here. For in our spiritual struggles, our emotions must be acknowledged. It's healthy to be completely honest before God. Cloistering now becomes a healing exercise requiring us to be still, basking ourselves in the Glory of His Grace, washing away our emotional anguish. I thank God!

ABOVE MY PAY GRADE
April 27, 2020

"The day has been long, the night is dark, but sleep does not easily come. So many thoughts, so many questions, so many concerns for loved ones and friends—for strangers and neighbors near and in faraway places. It is a strange and disturbing time for us. We are weary and frightened, yet hopeful and eager to hear some good news. We need daily reminders of your presence, frequent signs of your compassionate concern for humanity, evidence of your willingness to touch your creation with healing and life. It is so easy, too easy for us to forget. Like Simon Peter we tend to focus on the storm and not on you. So remind us again of your power and might—of your tender mercies and steadfast love. And send us, use us, help us to be living signs and reminders of your presence to others. Give us grace to let the light of your love shine in the darkness. And may the lights burn brighter and brighter until all shall see and know that you are Emmanuel, God with us, our hope, our salvation, our all. Amen."

—Thomas Patrick Nolan, April 27, 2020

Now is my moment in time while sheltering in place to wrestle with deeper thoughts than I usually do! I recall country doctor Dad's story of making a house call to a remote farm in Upshur County. The old farmer was studying on how to increase the water supply by digging the well deeper. Doc could not resist coming over to check it out. While standing on a mound of wet clay dirt extracted from the well, he slipped and fell down into the well. As the farmer pulled Doc out, all wet and dirty from the well, he said, "Doctors should tend the sick and leave the well alone!"

The question that keeps me awake at night has to do with the coronavirus pandemic. Are we to understand this scourge as the "day of our Lord"? Araceli lies beside me sleeping, with our cats Boots and Tail sleeping at our feet. They do not have a restless spirit about this historic moment in time. But a widespread divine reckoning against evil strikes me as a possibility. After all, I have spent 50 years giving tender loving medical and psychiatric care to victims of mean and nasty perpetrators. I have seen evil have its way with sweet and innocent children. When does the scale of justice get tipped toward hope and rescue?

The "day of our Lord" could rightfully come. That is what I am thinking in the dark, quiet midnight hour tucked under three quilts—but the thought is above my pay grade. So I need to study on it. I need to recall the lessons learned when earning my liberal arts education.

I crawl out of my comfort zone, shivering in the cool spring air, and click on the reading lamp by my side of the bed. The setup indicates this is not the first time I have pondered in the night. Now I reach for the Bible in large print, a consolation prize for growing old, and search for Zephaniah in the Old Testament. I remember having earlier questions concerning the "day of the Lord," which I asked as I studied religion under Dr. Peter Bercovitz at West Virginia Wesleyan College. This erudite professor remains one of my favorite gentle people, someone I admired for obscure reasons, like the fact that he rode a bike from home to campus as I also did. And he had a sense of humor. On one occasion when an actor portraying Samuel Clemens, aka Mark Twain, came to Wesleyan to entertain and educate us, Peter and Bea, his wife, sat with us students. We enjoyed it too much, laughing loudly at the remark: "The Bible is difficult to understand. But what bothers me," the actor dramatically said, "is not the part I do not understand about the Bible, but rather the part I do understand."

Directed by Dr. Bercovitz more than 50 years ago, tonight in the middle of the sheltering in place I rediscover Zephaniah. In three short chapters the prophet mentions the "day of the Lord" seven times. He has an inside track on

God's judgment on corruption and wickedness: "'When I destroy all mankind on the face of the earth,' declares the Lord, 'I will stretch out my hand against Judah and against all who live in Jerusalem'" (Zephaniah 1:3-4 NIV).

However, the book ends on a note of hope and rescue (3:18-20):

> "I will remove from you
>> all who mourn over the loss of your appointed festivals,
>> which is a burden and reproach for you.
> At that time I will deal
>> with all who oppressed you.
> I will rescue the lame;
>> I will gather the exiles.
> I will give them praise and honor
>> in every land where they have suffered shame.
> At that time I will gather you;
>> at that time I will bring you home.
> I will give you honor and praise
>> among all the peoples of the earth
> when I restore your fortunes
>> before your very eyes,"
>>> says the Lord.

Once again—needing to repeat a lesson until I learn it—I come back to the theme of the "day of our Lord." Yes, I know the plague encompassing our earth could represent fulfillment of prophecy. But I realize the answers to my questions involve a higher level of responsibility than I have. God only knows. The answer I search for is way above my pay grade.

THE REALLY OLD NORMAL:
AS OLD AS MOSES
April 28, 2020

The coronavirus has spread, putting the whole world in crisis. But we are not helpless. And we are not hopeless. We are just on a journey with an uncharted path. Moses gave us a guide as he recorded his speeches to the Jewish tribes in Deuteronomy. Actually, Moses gave us many clues for dealing with an enemy like COVID-19 by writing five books of the Bible, now called the Pentateuch.

The "really old normal" (as opposed to the "new normal" talked about by TV commentators and editorial writers) first for former Egyptian slaves, and second for us living through the current chaos, is to obey God's instruction: "And the Lord, he it is that doth go before thee; he will be with thee, he will not fail thee, neither forsake thee: fear not, neither be dismayed" (Deuteronomy 31:8 KJV).

Actually Araceli and I are pleased that Moses can be called "Doctor Moses." He was highly educated in Egyptian medical science as an adopted son in Pharaoh's court. We are similarly educated as physicians. His privileged learning from his beginning in the bulrushes along the Nile was a miracle. His instruction in diet and hygiene stands the test of time. Even his instruction on avoiding plagues is quite timely. Behavioral modification remains a foundation for us, now in social distancing and hand washing.

Our doctor connection to Moses extends to our wonderful West Virginia farm that we fondly call "The Promised Land." We honor Dr. Moses. These 182 acres of "almost Heaven" can be seen from the top of Mount Nebo in Upshur County.

When Araceli and I took the pilgrimage of a lifetime in 2015 to the Holy Land, we extended our time by crossing the Jordan River and climbing to the top of the original Mount Nebo. We stood where Moses stood before the budding

Hebrew nation to give his final leadership speech, including Deuteronomy chapter 31 noted above.

Looking down from the lofty heights in the modern nation of Jordan, we looked across the panorama: Gilead to the right; the Dead Sea to the left; the Jordan River below; Jericho just beyond the Jordan; Bethany at the top of the winding Jericho road; in the distant highlands, Jerusalem, and the Mediterranean Sea on the horizon. Just like in West Virginia, we looked down on the Promised Land. What a blessing!

Apropos to dealing with the current coronavirus pandemic, we looked up at a tall pole on the pinnacle, atop the pole a snake. The healing symbol's origin is recorded in Numbers 21:8 (KJV): "And the LORD said unto Moses, Make thee a fiery serpent, and set it upon a pole: and it shall come to pass, that every one that is bitten, when he looketh upon it, shall live."

God used Dr. Moses to bring about the curing of snake bites and gave us the modern symbol of medicine. Again we honor Dr. Moses with our emblem. He recorded a number of other treatments that work for ailments other than poisonous snake bites as well. We keep a copy of a book outlining the Biblical principles for good health, many from the writings of Moses. *None of These Diseases* by S.I McMillen, MD, is in our medical library, reminding us to turn to God at times like our current scourge.

The really old normal way of living soundly is truly our new normal. God's "fear not" taken in daily doses liberally will see us through any ailment including our coronavirus pandemic. God the Creator remains the Sustainer. Our response is one of faith—walking the uncharted path to the edge of all the light we can see; then taking the next step holding God's hand into the Promised Land. A prescription as old as Moses.

BEAUTIFUL FEET
May 5, 2020

How beautiful upon the mountains are the feet of him that bringeth good tidings, that publisheth peace; that bringeth good tidings of good, that publisheth salvation; that saith unto Zion, Thy God reigneth!

(Isaiah 52:7 KJV)

Here we are in very high stress environments and with recurrent traumatizations from the scourge that is the coronavirus pandemic. Probably about a third of us are affected in a way that makes it hard to function. We experience traumatic stress, emotional numbing, burnout, depression, insomnia, stress symptoms, and spiritual struggles. Certainly we need to hear "good tidings, that publisheth peace; that bringeth good tidings of good, that publisheth salvation; that saith unto Zion, Thy God reigneth!"

Just at the darkest moment before the dawn I hear something. A dream? A vision? Listen: I hear the pitter patter of feet upon the mountain. Surely a shoeless person. A distant call coming closer:

"Thy God reigneth!"

"Thy God reigneth!"

"Thy God reigneth!"

A barefoot messenger dances along the upward trail. Ahead on the path startled deer scatter fallen leaves, creating rustling sounds. Hearken to the newly returned migrant birds singing out a clarion call, announcing a runner picking up an ever-quickening pace. Bunny rabbits scamper off the trail in a zigzag pattern. Squirrels scoot up into the forest overstory, chirping loudly once safe above the fracas.

The barefoot healer runs boldly toward our destructive pandemic scene. Fearless, bold, brave, called the Hebrew word *mebasser*: messenger of good news!

"Ironic" is my first thought. Yet so perfect.

"Barefoot" is my second thought. "Not my idea of physical beauty, yet how beautiful!"

"However, an answer to prayer, for we are in trouble!" is my third thought.

To a viral infected person, racked with fever, dying of thirst, begging for salvation—small matter that the feet are bare and the cup of water taken from the hand-pumped well would be in an old, chipped and soiled ladle.

My soul grieves the headline that April 21, 2020, Holocaust Remembrance Day—*Yom HaShoah* in Hebrew—is to be exclusively celebrated by digital communication due to the horrible coronavirus pandemic. No survivors on pilgrimage; no concentration camp tours; no interviews learning the lessons of how children survived. However, I can smile with survivors of imprisonment in the Nazi death camps who recall the American GIs who liberated them were the most beautiful sight they have ever, ever seen—even though the GIs needed a shave and shower and were clothed in olive-drab uniforms.

So it is in the Isaiah 52:7 text! Lo the exiles, who have lost all hope that they might ever be free again, look out across the mountain and see the one who announces peace and good news and salvation. The otherwise sight for sore eyes is beautiful—right down to His feet.

Caring for American heroes as a psychiatrist at the Veterans' Hospital, I have listened to some great stories. One GI who suffered frostbite in the Battle of the Bulge fighting the Germans to the bitter end went to see his medic. He received the most outlandish advice, being told he must keep his feet dry. No extra socks; no petroleum salve; no heat to warm his feet. Keep his feet dry! That day in my office I asked him if I might examine his feet. I stooped to assist removing the shoes and socks of this elderly veteran. What I saw shocked me. The skin still showed a deep blue-gray discoloration. Three toes were missing, leaving deep ulcerations thinly coated. There were no nail beds. I found myself crying loudly but exclaiming through the tears, "How beautiful upon the mountains are the feet of him that bringeth good tidings, that publisheth peace; that bringeth good tidings of good, that publisheth salvation; that saith unto Zion, Thy God reigneth."

BALM FOR ALL PEOPLE
May 15, 2020

1 Sing to the LORD a new song; sing to the LORD, all the earth.
...

3 Declare his glory among the nations, his marvelous deeds among all peoples.
...

7 Ascribe to the LORD, all you families of nations, ascribe to the LORD glory and strength.
...

11 Let the heavens rejoice, let the earth be glad; let the sea resound, and all that is in it.
...

13 Let all creation rejoice before the LORD, for he comes, he comes to judge the earth. He will judge the world in righteousness and the peoples in his faithfulness.

(Psalm 96 NIV)

"All people" come under the purview of God. The sanctuary of First United Methodist Church in Buckhannon has wonderful stained glass windows. High above the sanctuary is the eye of God looking down on all the seats where worshipers gather. And every United States $1 bill features the "Eye of Providence" symbol, which represents the eye of God watching over humanity. And our nation's motto, also found printed on our currency, is "In God We Trust"!

Psalm 96 is a majestic song of God's inclusive intention. The theme is clear: "All" people and "all" the Earth! Just like the artistic portrayal of the eye of God watching ALL, so now we have another ALL. We now have a coronavirus pandemic affecting ALL the people on this spinning Earth, third rock from the sun. Yes, we have a historic footnote of the Spanish Flu killing millions just over 100 years ago, but nothing like this has happened recently.

In medical terms we have words describing treatments for disease states. "Salve" etymology from Old English notes a healing balm for the body. In spiritual terms we have "salvation" etymology arising from Latin indicating the saving of the soul. Such words get reworked in the midst of our current plague for an online source of information regarding our coronavirus pandemic titled "Virtual Salve" at salve.edu/virtual-salve. I enjoy the creative spirit bubbling forth.

The largest organ of the human body is our skin. Treatment for the skin, therefore, gets much attention. Infection often shows signs and symptoms involving the skin, as in measles and chicken pox. Healing balms often are prescribed. Sometimes these relieve suffering, but sometimes not. Thus these balms could be hawked by a "quacksalver," from Dutch/Germanic roots. Word usage now shortens this to imply a treatment by a charlatan or just a "quack."

Popular writers creatively deal with pandemics, too. One of the poems I memorized in the 7th grade for my outstanding English teacher Virginia Bly Hoover was "The Raven." In 1845 Edgar Allan Poe seemed to be seeking healing as he mentioned "balm in Gilead" in one of the last stanzas of his poem:

"Prophet!" said I, "thing of evil!- prophet still, if bird or devil!-
Whether Tempter sent, or whether tempest tossed thee here ashore,
Desolate yet all undaunted, on this desert land enchanted-
On this home by horror haunted- tell me truly, I implore-
Is there- is there balm in Gilead?- tell me- tell me, I implore!"
Quoth the Raven, "Nevermore."

Likewise the African-American Spirituals in our culture have powerful references to healing salve or balm with lyrics like this:

There is a balm in Gilead
To make the wounded whole;
There is a balm in Gilead
To heal the sin-sick soul.

Some times I feel discouraged,
And think my work's in vain,
But then the Holy Spirit
Revives my soul again.

If you cannot sing like angels,
If you can't preach like Paul,
You can tell the love of Jesus,
And say He died for all.

Establishing an etymological foundation encompassing the whole world, now I return to our coronavirus pandemic. Medically this is primarily a respiratory illness. Most disease states are mild, but some are severe. Araceli and I fall into the senior age which means we may get severe disease. So while there are coronavirus symptoms which primarily are typical of a respiratory syndrome, we are in a state of heightened awareness for emergency symptoms which require medical assistance:

- Trouble breathing
- Constant pain or pressure in your chest
- Bluish lips or face
- Sudden confusion

"Bluish lips or face" is a grave sign directly observed involving our skin. In the case of COVID-19, the skin color change relates to poor oxygen saturation and exchange in the lungs. I call attention to this sign due to my attention to skin treatments with salves or balms.

I return to Psalm 96, for I believe in healing of the body and the soul for ALL people. Certainly the Scripture is clear that God chose Abraham as the father of His chosen people. Yet God never intended salvation to be the exclusive claim of the Hebrew nation. From start to finish of this majestic Psalm of praise, I see God's gracious inclusion of everyone who will believe. The psalm begins, "Sing to the Lord, all the earth." Verse 3 charges God's people to "declare his glory among the nations." Verse 7 calls on "all you families of nations" to praise God. The psalm concludes, "He will judge the world in righteousness and the peoples in his faithfulness."

God's plan is plain. The big picture for our scourge of the coronavirus pandemic is also plain. Both are inclusive. May God in His mercy heal us ALL!

THE SERENITY PRAYER
May 18, 2020

God, grant me the serenity to accept the things I cannot change, courage to change the things I can, and wisdom to know the difference.

The Serenity Prayer is a prayer written by the American theologian Reinhold Niebuhr (1892-1971). At this time of coronavirus pandemic shelter-in-place, my self-imposed lifestyle charting would not be complete if I did not examine myself in light of this prayer. The Serenity Prayer has so influenced my professional psychiatric medicine practice treating substance abuse disorders.

Half joking, I told my dear wife, Araceli, that we have lived under the influence of the practice of medicine. The demands to time and energy are tremendous. In one sense practicing medicine had become one of the gods in our lives prior to Araceli's retirement Memorial Day 2007, on the occasion of daughter Maria's wedding to Justin. My wise wife prepped me for my retirement when she put family first. I made my decision around the request of son Ronce and his wife Yasmine to come to Washington, DC, to nurture granddaughter Harper Rose during March 2015. Ronce's work took him out of the country for an airline safety audit, and Yasmine's work also took her abroad for an international space launch. Granddaughter care trumped medical care—a wise decision.

We began a process of disengaging. Araceli and I disengaged from medicine not because we were burned out or that we had to. We did so for a higher purpose. We wished to become Lola and Lolo to our granddaughters. We wished to flourish in God's garden planted by the still waters surrounded by green pastures. Sheltering-in-place allows the pause to disengage from destructive relationships and unhealthy habits and to delight in God's instruction.

Obviously in 2020, our world has come to a halt due to the contagious virus infecting citizens of 184 countries. Whatever might have been gods—whether sexuality, money, work, power, alcohol or other drugs, relationships, sports, theater, or other activities—matter not now. "The saw cuts both ways" is a West Virginia mountaineer way of saying these type of gods might have been dominating some folks' thinking, emotions and actions, representing addictions and dependencies potentially.

"God, grant me the serenity to accept the things I cannot change." Shelter-in-place has shifted life back from being dangerously out of balance to a time of re-balance.

As a practicing psychiatrist, I knew a crisis would bring the next patient into my office. Life can be like that. Of course, some would not come even when they would have benefited from self-examination leading to acceptance of change. But when the suffering soul arrived, the path to healing would begin.

My work was to listen. Sometimes I added a statement like, "Life is what it is," if the patient needed a punctuation to their story. But I did not dare interrupt the narrative.

By listening intentionally, I gained the right to propose that this would be hard work we were undertaking. What my patient needed to say eventually to himself/herself was: "May I have the courage to change the things I can."

Usually by the tenth session there was an "aha moment." Their sheltering-in-place had taken place either in the sanctuary of my office or in the protection of a caring hospital ward. The patient would see the light of what was controlling them, asking not simply if something was right or wrong, but where it would lead. The path may have been leading to suicide.

Then, for timing is everything, the rest of Reinhold Niebuhr's prayer could be voiced: "Grant me ... wisdom to know the difference." In terms of psycho (soul) therapy, my suffering patient would position himself/herself in a new posture so as to know wisdom.

The Serenity Prayer ultimately turns a life around from a pathway toward destruction to a new path flourishing in a Higher Power's attentiveness. The Master Gardener—God—watches and guides toward a better way, a more fruitful way.

For me, drawing close to our granddaughters has been sheer delight. I balance my life through writing short stories for them. I meditate with Aliza, Harper Rose, Emilia and Camille in mind. The Hebrew word used for meditate means "to mutter." Some days I am talking to myself but really to them. Sheltering-in-place makes time to become deliberate and thoughtful; it's comparable to the act of studying. Prayerfully staying in God's Word is most practical for my study. I believe Reinhold Niebuhr might agree.

LESSON LEARNED SERVING ON
THE BOARD OF EDUCATION: #347
Weekly newspaper column in the *Record Delta*
May 29, 2020

We are surrounded by suffering due to COVID-19, so this is a proper time to examine the concept of pain as a lesson learned. This coronavirus pandemic has caused much suffering and pain. I see growing evidence every day as I continue serving as an elected member of our Upshur County Schools Board of Education (BOE). At our May 5th public meeting, we were hampered in our desire to convey emotionally the gratitude we feel in our hearts by the limitations of our use of Microsoft TEAMS technology, necessary because of this very contagious virus. My pain was a heartache. Our 2020 retirees who have given a lifetime of service could not be honored in person. Certainly we could not hug or hand shake or back slap our dedicated teachers and service personnel. Those retirees who planned on traveling to visit grandchildren or tour sights of interest will not be able to enjoy that long-awaited pleasure. And what about our Buckhannon-Upshur High School class of 2020 graduates? They have been denied a Prom and a final Honors Assembly and so much more recognizing their years of journey to "destination graduation." These are real examples of pain.

Of course we have lost the actual chance to visit at the bedside with loved ones who have become infected with the coronavirus or to attend funerals of those who have succumbed to the disease. Their suffering must only be imagined as they struggled to breathe and to bear the aches and pains of the virus made worse by their isolation. I feel a deep pain in my soul.

Part of our BOE meeting includes board member comments. For several meetings, I have addressed the issue of pain and suffering. My entire professional career as a medical doctor has been devoted to relieving suffering. I feel extremely hampered in our present condition. In my remarks at the close of our BOE meetings, I look for ways to see the silver lining in the cloud. I seek ways to encourage our students to examine their hearts. Just maybe some students will decide to devote their life energy to relieving suffering and pain. Maybe our students will have a heart tug as they recognize the healthcare heroes running to defeat this worldwide scourge, some falling ill and dying from the plague they are fighting. Who will carry on? Perhaps an Upshurite student will vow to become a healthcare provider who in future battles with infection and death will fill the ranks of the fallen who gave all! Vowing to carry on the battle treating the contagious patients, relieving their suffering, may become a calling in this hour of extreme pain.

May the mission of some Buckhannon-Upshur students be "to cure sometimes, to relieve often, to comfort always." During this time of pain, may they vow to prepare their hearts and minds for the healing professions. May these tender young lives feel a social responsibility to become a healthcare worker or a first responder. I can say as a healer who has finished my own course, this decision made today will fully engage our students who answer the call.

LESSON LEARNED SERVING ON THE BOARD OF EDUCATION: #352
Weekly newspaper column in the *Record Delta*
June 25, 2020

Our Upshur County Schools Reentry Advisory Council met virtually using TEAMS technology on June 5, 2020. That we are still not meeting in person due to the coronavirus pandemic says a whole bunch about the obstacles we face in opening schools in the fall. Dr. Sara Lewis Stankus and Dr. Jeff Harvey serve as facilitators for our Council, which is made up of leading professionals representing our Buckhannon-Upshur community. Getting from "virtual" to "schools open" remains an uncharted reentry. Lesson Learned as a West Virginia doctor growing up during other epidemics, I offer up that communicating plainly is vital to our success as we chart our return to school.

My childhood had a dark cloud hanging over known as the polio epidemic. One classmate suffered paralysis, and another classmate's older brother had to leave home to live out his shortened life in an iron lung in a far-removed city. Sad indeed. Hope for us Academy Grade School students came with the Salk polio vaccine. Around our family supper table I heard Country Doc Dad tell Mom that up to 200,000 new infantile paralysis cases occurred yearly. Polio still exists but, thank God, the vaccines saved much suffering.

Our children and grandchildren will have various takes on the current pandemic. Little Granddaughter Harper Rose was asked by our son Roncevert over a recent meal what COVID-19 meant to her. She observed that having her mother and father work from home was appealing to her: "We are closer as a family!"

Another granddaughter, Aliza, has also benefited from the quarantine at home due to creative encouragement by Mommy Maria and Daddy Justin. Ever since an international trip to her Grandmother Lola's home country of the

Philippine Islands, Aliza has wanted to become an architect. Her mind fills with housing improvements for Filipino children. Sparked by genuine caring, she has created double-decker hammocks, improved bird nests, and done some very basic engineering projects with her sister, Emilia. She announces now she will be an architectural engineer. Upon my word—growth and development beyond expectations!

For sure, families will do what families have always done—decide based on the best information available how to act for the sake of their children. Also, the Upshur County Schools Board of Education has said again and again that we make our BOE decisions for the sake of the students!

My educated gut reaction is that opening school in the fall will remain a goal but will not be smooth until we have a vaccine. Dr. Joseph Reed, our Upshur-Buckhannon Health Department Medical Director, points out how social distancing might be maintained. (Note that he is speaking personally, not giving official recommendations.) He suggests students come part time, for example 1/3 of the students at a time and live stream to the other 2/3 who are not physically in class. That would give two days of classroom instruction for each of our nearly 4,000 students, allowing spacing on school buses and in school classrooms. That would also mean Saturday classes for some. We could serve one area of the county each day and thus also significantly reduce transportation costs overall. The public health model would mean all wearing cloth masks, washing hands frequently, and checking temperatures before coming onto the buses. These are certainly reasonable steps in the face of a worldwide virus infection that we must respect.

Stay tuned, more to come.

Aliza Eloise Almond Pope, age 8

Emilia Sylvie Almond Pope, age 6

"Healing, Health, and Wholeness
of
Body, Mind, and Spirit"

Camp Farthest Out
July 1999

WV Summer Family CFO presentation
July 19, 1999

I want to start with something I appreciate all the time. And that is: God is good all the time. All the time. God is good, all the time. Amen.

Billboards for God

The *New York Times* had a headline: "Billboards From God; Did Somebody Say, 'Give Me a Sign, Lord'?" Someone with a dream in Florida put up $150,000 to an ad agency to create inter-denominational messages about God being good all the time. The ad agency came up with these ads and won an OBIE award, basically the Oscars of the advertising world. That's why it made the *New York Times* Sunday edition, probably the most-read Sunday paper in the world. This has been picked up all across the country. Some 15 million dollars of ads have run such as these:

"Do you have any idea of where you're going?" -God
"Let's meet at my house Sunday before the game." -God
"Come on over and bring the kids." -God
"What part of 'thou shall not' didn't you understand?" -God
"Loved the wedding. Invite me to the marriage." -God
"That 'love thy neighbor' thing, I meant it." -God
"I love you, I love you, I love you." -God
"Will the road you're on get you to my place?" -God
"Follow me." -God
"My way is the high way." -God

"Need directions?" -God
"Tell the kids I love them." -God
"You think it's hot here?" -God
"Need a marriage counselor? I'm available." -God
"Have you read my number one bestseller? There will be a test." -God
"I don't question your existence." -God
"I can think of ten things that are carved in stone." -God
"We need to talk." -God

So one man in Florida had a vision, put up a little money, and the vision has grown.

Jesus, our wounded healer

I worked at the VA Hospital in Clarksburg for a long time. I've always thought that this body, mind, and spirit idea was the only way to go with healing, with practicing medicine, with ministry. We spent two days working out a mission statement and a vision statement. I got into the VA's vision statement that we are here, we exist for the purpose of healing body, mind and spirit. We have to bring it into reality, but that's up to God.

This week I would like to talk about healing principles. My father passed away this spring. He practiced medicine for 41 years in Buckhannon, and I had a golden opportunity to be an associate of his for 9 years. It was a real education. After he passed away I began to work on my own grief and loss. The Scriptures are very clear about the idea of a wounded healer. "By Christ's stripes we are healed." It is very evident that we serve a wounded healer. Our healing is more sure, you could say, than our salvation, because when Jesus was alive even on this earth, He already made preparation for our healing. Of course with His death and resurrection we have eternal life and life forever.

We have so many blessings, and they are all tied together. But the idea of the wounded healer has always been there. In fact, you can go back to Babylon and to King Nebuchadnezzar looking into the fiery furnace in the book of Daniel. The king said, "Look! I see four men walking around in the fire, unbound and unharmed, and the fourth looks like a son of the gods" (Daniel 3:25 NIV). Of course the church has always thought that fourth person was Christ. He came into the world, and He came into the furnace which is the world, and He experienced and suffered all that the world offers, all that intensity, that hatred that so many people have when they lash out and wound other people because they hate themselves. From the very time He was born, He experienced the furnace. King Herod killed all the male youth under two years old in an attempt to kill Jesus. That was a horrible furnace for the mothers and fathers and families of that time. Jesus came into that. And then all the violence that is in the world, he experienced. All those ancient animosities don't go away. We experience them everyday. The idea of the wounded healer is very evident.

Our senior psychiatrist at Oral Roberts University's City of Faith Hospital, Dr. George Parkhurst, built our psychiatric program on Camp Farthest Out Christian principles. That was the way he practiced psychiatry. We did "devotion and emotion" every morning with our patients. We sang wonderful charismatic songs. We had creative activities every day for our patients. I had the pleasure of being there for two years working with George. So the things I'm going to share about healing, I've seen many, many times. Dr. Parkhurst was 77 years old at this time. Many people would be retired at that point. But he said that he never came to work until he was in the Spirit; he never missed work, and he was always in the Spirit! He got there through some of the principles that I am going to begin to teach tonight that I saw at work.

I live in Buckhannon. When I was just a youth, West Virginia Wesleyan College was building Wesley Chapel, which is a marvelous church. I was active in our Methodist youth ministry. I was asked to be part of the cornerstone laying, representing the youth of West Virginia on the cornerstone. You can see it if you go there today. There is a quote by John Wesley. It is simply about being in the Spirit: "The best of all is, God is with us." That's right in the cornerstone of the church. Dr. Parkhurst had a banner hanging on his wall, a scroll, with the words, "Christ was born for this." At the bottom was a nail dangling down. Christ was born for this, the wounded healer.

My daughter Maria sent me a mystical poem from the *Oxford Book of English Mystical Verse* by Irish writer Oscar Wilde. This is from his poem *E Tenebris:*

> Come down, O Christ, and help me! reach thy hand,
> For I am drowning in a stormier sea
> Than Simon on thy lake of Galilee:
> The wine of life is spilt upon the sand,
> My heart is as some famine-murdered land,
> Whence all good things have perished utterly,
> And well I know my soul in Hell must lie
> If I this night before God's throne should stand.
> "He sleeps perchance, or rideth to the chase,
> Like Baal, when his prophets howled that name
> From morn to noon on Carmel's smitten height."
> Nay, peace, I shall behold before the night,
> The feet of brass, the robe more white than flame,
> The wounded hands, the weary human face.

The attributes of God and staying in the Spirit

Christ is with us all the time. So how did Dr. Parkhurst, or how do I, get in the Spirit every day? We're going to do a little exercise here. You may want to keep this and use it for mediation. By the way, I borrowed this from Bill Bright's book *GOD: Discover His Character*. I brought along a medical journal. I just picked this up: *The American Academy of Family Physicians*. This is the way I'm going to read a medical journal. I'm going to turn to a section on the various articles. I might start by reading an article on the pathogens associated with infected dog and cat bites. This is a good summer topic. I learn in my article that there are 300,000 visits made to the emergency room due to animal bites—10,000 people are hospitalized and 20 die. Then I remember that man's best friend is the dog. Then I think about God; because God is a person, I can know Him intimately. So God can be my best friend. Your mind starts to be immersed in spiritual things even as you look at something like a medical article.

Let me read an article about the treatment of panic disorder and Prozac. There are 6 billion people on earth, and there are 2 billion prescriptions for Prozac. There's something about the fiery furnace that we live in, the stress, that so many people are turning to Prozac. I've already started thinking about God as I'm reading about Prozac. Then I would turn to an attribute of God. In Bright's book *GOD: Discover His Character,* the first point is: "Because God is all-powerful, He can help me with anything." He is more powerful than Prozac.

Then I might go to an article on beer, wine and liquor and decreased risk of myocardial infarction. All my alcoholic patients want to tell me about this article: "You can drink and it will help your heart!" Well, maybe. There are other spirits in life, so my mind would switch over to a second attribute of God: "Because God is present everywhere, He is always present with me." Or as Wesley said, "The best of all is, God is with us." The attributes of God come out even as I might begin to think about something to do with medicine.

I might come to another article, and I'm just doing this exercise by flipping pages. This is how you can get into the Spirit so easily. Everything goes back to God, that is the point. Here is one about wound infections and antibiotics. It talks about a number of people in a double-blind study, and then I realize that these medicines are made from plants that

God made. Another attribute from Bright comes to my mind: "Because God knows everything, I will go to Him with all my questions and concerns." I can remember a diabetic ulcer we treated at the City of Faith. It was a miracle of healing. A lady came in with a horrible leg wound. The number one reason for amputations in our country is diabetes, and it is the number one cause for blindness and so many sorrows and pains. This lady had a horrible leg ulcer, and we didn't know what to do. We could put a medicine on the leg, but we didn't have any hope that we could save her leg. But we could pray about it. The next morning, it was the nicest baby's skin you would ever want to see. No sign of infection. God knows everything.

I might go to another article. This would be adherence to treatment to prevent depression relapse. We know that people who become depressed can become depressed again. About 50 percent of the time they do, according to the article. But we also know that through AA and other 12-step programs that you have to trust the higher power, that is God. Then I would go to the next attribute: "Because God is sovereign, I will joyfully submit to His will." We can overcome depression by keeping and staying with God all the time. He is sovereign. So even as I read an article about relapse, my mind turns back to God.

Then I come to an article on steroids and helping children with asthma. It is a very big deal. We have too many particles in the air, so many kids have asthma. The number one thing we're taught as family doctors is that whatever you do, don't let an asthmatic child play sports without having their inhaler at their side, because kids die every year from asthma attacks. As I think about breathing, I recall that God breathed into us. Attribute six: "Because God is holy, I will devote myself to Him in purity, worship and service." We need to say, "Breathe on me, breath of God." This is the way your mind goes back and forth. You can go all through these articles. And you can match them to attributes of God. Again,

I credit Bill Bright and his book *GOD: Discover His Character*.

So there are ways to begin to meditate on the attributes of God. That becomes something that you start thinking about all the time. It never stops, and it always is revealing. It's absolutely amazing the way it happens. I like the story of Corrie Ten Boom. As a child she was afraid of what would happen in the future. Her father comforted her by asking her a question: "When we're going to take a trip on the train, when do I give you your ticket?"

She thought a minute and said, "Right before I get on the train, so I don't lose it."

He replied, "Yes, and that is what our Heavenly Father does. He knows exactly what we need and when we need it, and He gives it to us at the exact right time."

We know that God's timing is perfect. We know what we need to do next by staying close to God. If we're in the Spirit every moment, then we will know what we need to know at the right time. Active meditation on God is so important for our healing, our well-being, our ministry.

Working as a Christian healer

As healers, we get a lot of direction from songs. I came across this song that a minister put in the bulletin recently, shortly after my father passed away. I needed some healing. It just happened to be the song we sang that Sunday: "O Christ the Healer" written by Fred Pratt Green in 1967. God knew I would need it in 1999.

I thought about my father as a Christian gentleman and as a physician. My mother was very supportive of his role as a country doctor. We would always have supper together. That was our family time. We always had meals and always had prayer and devotion time. That might be the only time we would see Dad all day. He would always lead us in praying a simple prayer:

86

God is great, and God is good,
and we thank Him for our food;
By His blessings we are fed.
Give us Lord, our daily bread. Amen.

I thought about this simple prayer—he was praying about our whole salvation. Love is reaching to us with blessings like restoration, like healing, like this daily meal.

I think back to working 4-H camps in the summer. They gave me the assignment of working the sheep barn at the state fair. It was a fascinating thing. I now understand the 23rd Psalm very well. I know what the psalmist knew. The men who were showing these prize-winning sheep bathed their sheep every day, but the men didn't take a bath all week. I know because I slept in the loft with them! There were 300 sheep *baahing* down there, but if their sheep would *baah* in a certain way, they would know their voice and they would go check to see what was wrong with their sheep. Among all that cacophony of sounds that I couldn't stand, trying to sleep with all those sheep *baahing* all the time, they knew and would answer their sheep's call of distress. I pray almost every day that I am the sheep and God is the shepherd, and ask Him to lead me to the right pasture and the right task. That's the way we live.

I asked my father about why he made house calls for 42 years. It's not really an efficient way to practice medicine. You can stay in your office and see a lot of people quickly. If you have ever gone to a doctor, you see how quickly they can see you. My dad said that he would learn so much from his patients by being in their homes. He would see where they live, whether they are keeping their house up, if they have a garden, and so many things that he would never know if they just came to the office. He would actually be able to heal them. It would be more efficient in the long run. Of course there were other things in the older days. The party-line system helped. One patient would call from up in the country and everyone else would be listening. So they all would be out there waving. He would see various people as he was going up the road in his Jeep. He ran a little clinic; by the time he got up and down the road he had seen half a dozen people, not just the one patient. But his philosophy of care gets to the heart of this: "I always want to exceed my patients' expectations." He knew they didn't just need the physical touch. They needed someone to encourage them. We have many nurses in our county. Many of them have been coming up to me in the last two months saying, "Your father told me I would be a good nurse when I was six years old. Now I'm a nurse." They are proud of it. He was right, the Holy Spirit was right. I don't go and tell them, "Well, he told a thousand other little girls the same thing!" Literally he and two other doctors delivered 12,000 babies in our county, and there are only 20,000 people in the county. He did tell a lot of people they would make a good nurse. He knew they had a deeper need. They needed someone to listen to them, to encourage them.

There is a museum in Pickens, West Virginia, which incidentally has the smallest high school in the US. I think they make the national news every year when they graduate one or two people from high school. It's so remote that they can't close the school because no kid should ride three hours in one direction to get to a high school, so they let them go to all 12 grades in one room. Anyway, Dad was up there at Pickens at their Maple Syrup Festival. I went with him last year, the last time he went. This example drives home in my mind this idea of always giving more than the patient would expect. A woman we met recalled when she was a 3- or 4-year-old child, it was one of her earliest memories. She had some type of an illness, a fever and bellyache and things that she might need a doctor for. She was a foster child; she didn't know who her parents were. She was living with people that had taken her in. They were poor tenant farmers. They didn't even own their own land. They were living in a shack on the other side of the mountain from the road. So apparently Dad had to walk up over a hill and down a hill a mile and a half to take care of this little girl. He usually gave a shot of penicillin in these cases. Then it was late, and he spent the night to see if she was going to be okay. The lady of the house prepared breakfast.

So this girl is now middle aged, and she came up to Dad and said, "I just want to tell you how grateful I am, how you saved my life and changed my life in so many ways. Do you remember that?"

Dad said, "Yeah, your mother served the best pancakes and sausage and biscuits."

The lady said, "Yeah, you do remember."

That's the type of care that you can't put a cost on. But if you're going to go into healing, really want to be a healer, this is what I'm talking about.

I'm going to give you an exercise tomorrow about how you can get deeper. I think it will be helpful in disclosing, sometimes even to yourself. There are some things that we know that no one else knows, and there are some things about ourselves that we don't know that other people do know. Then obviously there are things that we don't know and no one else knows; they are known only to God. I want to have an exercise with you about that.

But for my father, this growth that he had that helped him become a healer was the Great Depression. Most of us don't know what that would ever be like. As a high school student, he was a caddy. He had saved $50 from caddying, which was a lot of money in those days. He remembered when the Great Depression came, he was living in Maplewood, a community in Newark just outside New York City. Some of the people he used to caddy for were jumping off buildings, killing themselves. They had no hope, they were losing everything. They had $50, and they lived on that for six months. That's all the money his family had. Of course it slowed down his life. He had to spend seven years working before he could ever think about going to college and continuing his education. He did that by helping to develop the Appalachian Trail. He was one of the people that built the trail from New York to Maine. He spent a year or more in a fire tower in Vermont. He could not come down unless it rained because someone had to watch the forest in case there was any type of fire. At the time, someone from Harvard came up with a list of the 100 greatest books ever written, the classics in literature. During that year Dad read all of them. So he got an education even as he was waiting to get an education. There are truths that are unconscious, that even our pride would resist. We wouldn't want to know them, those things about ourselves. We wouldn't want to get that deep into ourselves. But it made him strong.

Then came World War II. We stand on the shoulders of this generation that helped us so much. My father and the healers that came out of this generation developed who they were from suffering, from being wounded, and they were healed. They had the healing truth given to them by God.

This is the age of anxiety, the age of depression. I read various Christian journals, and you cannot tell from surveys who is a Christian and who is not a Christian by the number of divorces, infidelity, bankruptcies, adolescent pregnancies, whatever marker you want to call. You cannot tell a Christian from a non-Christian. And yet we are called to be separate people. We have so many conflicts that would destroy our health. We have the world's disease.

What is the cure? It is the deeper walk that we are talking about, the constant meditation. I can think of an example from my father and other people of that generation separating themselves from their community and identifying themselves clearly as Christians. Probably more public health good has come from clean water supplies than anything else. Go back a little farther to Joseph Lister and the antiseptic surgery technique. And doctors learning to wash their hands when going from one delivery room to another saved a lot of babies and mothers. As soon as we knew about the germ theory, we could have clean water. Then we could purify our water. In the 1950s my mother and father were 4-H leaders. We needed a pool at our Upshur County Youth camp because the river was not fit to swim in, and a pool would be more sanitary. Also there was a polio epidemic at that time. Mothers and fathers feared the summertime because of paralytic polio. The vaccine came out, and we were trying to get the pool at the same time this was happening. My father and mother tried to get the community to come together. Pass a levy, and everyone would pay a little money through a tax and they would build a swimming pool for the community. They tried   levies which would share the burden, and they failed four times. They could not get the people to vote for it.

So Dad said, "Well, let's go ahead and vaccinate all the kids. Let's exceed everyone's expectations. Let's vaccinate every kid in the county for polio. We'll get the sugar cube vaccine that kids will like to take, drop the vaccine on the sugar cube. Then we'll put a 4-Her by the vaccine and put on a cup: 'Get your free vaccine and put a penny in the cup.'" They raised enough money to build a swimming pool: $30,000. They vaccinated every child in the county. That's separating yourself from the world's disease. Having a vision. And Christ is the cure.

Conclusion

I have a book, *Hallelujah Anyhow: Suffering in the Christian Community of Faith.* We went to see our daughter in England over spring break. I have an Irish friend, and my wife and I said, "We need to go to Northern Ireland." There was a war going on. Everyone said, "Don't go, don't go." When you feel safe with God you sometimes do daring things. My wife's best friend in our little town owns a computer business. It's well thought out, and she is very successful. Linda Wellings is the Businesswoman of the Year in West Virginia this year. She is a fine Christian lady. She actually developed, because of government grants, an opportunity to have an international computer company with an office in Northern Ireland, in Belfast. We knew that, so we said, "We'll go visit your business partner, Ian Sneddon." Beyond that, Ian also happened to be a Gideon. Gideons are very active in Northern Ireland giving out Bibles, as they do in other places. So we went to Northern Ireland and spent three days. We found the Christians under this fire that they are experiencing just like Daniel. God is with them, even in that country. We came across the Northern Irish Sea and Ian and his family met us at the dock. We were driving back to his house to spend the night, my family and I. He was showing us various things. He said, "Now don't get off at that section ever. That's where all the conflict is." We were out touring the next day, and I got lost and ended up there. I called him and he said, "Don't move, I'm coming down." He came and rescued us.

He gave us this old Gaelic blessing I want to share with you. Maybe this is about healing, too:

> May those who love us, love us.
> And those who don't love us,
> May God turn their hearts.
> And if He doesn't turn their hearts,
> May He turn their ankles,
> So we'll know them by their limping.

Well, we're going to go deeper tomorrow. I want to talk with you about a concept I learned a lot about at the City of Faith—*nephish*. It's the root word for the soul. I looked up just the first part of Psalm 103:

> Praise the Lord, my soul;
>   all my inmost being, praise His holy name.
> Praise the Lord, my soul,

and forget not all His benefits—
who forgives all your sins
and heals all your diseases,
who redeems your life from the pit
and crowns you with love and compassion,
who satisfies your desires with good things
So that your youth is renewed like the eagle's.

God is good, all the time. All the time, God is good.

---

*NOTE: For more in-depth study of God and His Character,
go to* https://discovergod.com/character/.

WV Summer Family CFO presentation
July 20, 1999

God is good, all the time. All the time, God is good. We've already had demonstrations of that. We were singing the song "Spirit of the Living God," and I read in the margin note that the author had wanted it to say, "Break me, melt me, mold me, fill me." We were talking about being broken, about suffering and about being a wounded healer last night. So praise God.

Strength in suffering
Another way that the Holy Spirit is speaking to me was that I was asked to reflect on the Beatitudes. They spoke to me, especially the 5th, 6th, and 10th verses of Matthew 5:

> Happy are those who mourn, for they shall be comforted.
> Happy are those who hunger and thirst for what is right, they shall be satisfied.
> Happy are those who are persecuted in the cause of right. Theirs is the kingdom of heaven.

This suffering that we go through, we can be "happy" about it because it arouses some type of inner strength within us. It clarifies why we are here, what we're all about. It's the fire that burns away all that is not important and deepens our sense of compassion.

From a doctor's standpoint, a patient is someone that suffers. I'm certified by the American Board of Psychiatry and Neurology. I remember when I took neurology in medical school, the professor said if you're going to be a neurologist, you have to have headaches. You can't understand headaches unless you have them yourself. You have to suffer that. I do have them. Fortunately I have found a cure for mine—I can run. When I start to jog, I suppose I balance my arteries and my headache goes away. Some people have to lie down in a dark room. But praise God, we understand suffering sometimes by going through suffering ourselves.

We are going to talk about the subconscious self that has this resiliency there, the vitality, the vital part of life. We who study the brain as a vital organ would consider the heart important, the liver important, all parts of the body important, but the brain is so important. This is the decade of the brain in medical research and science.

Who are we?

I collect papers. This is a very special day in the history of the U.S. I was looking at the *New York Times* Sunday edition, July 20th, 1969, the Apollo moon landing. It is the very day 30 years later. It seems like yesterday. The editorial in the *New York Times* says they landed in the sea of tranquility, and yet we don't have peace on earth. They left earth, and we don't have peace 30 years later. Then it says, "Who are we that such a thing as this is possible?" Who are we? We're creatures, creations of the living God. I remember a conversation about what questions we need to know from our veterans at the VA, what we want to teach them as we do a spiritual history. My contribution to that meeting was a reflection from a CFO conference where the speaker listed the questions we need to know: Who are we? Who are these other people around us? Who's in charge? That's the format. The *New York Times* editorial doesn't know who we are yet. But we know, and we are finding out day by day. That's the spiritual journey that we're on.

Well, how can we find out who we are? I want to talk about something that I discovered recently. How do we get deeper? David Seamands, a Methodist minister, wrote a book on inner healing called *Healing of Memories*. I remember a story that he told. He was a missionary in India, and the monsoon rains came. He had a Jeep, but finally the rain came so much and the mud was so deep that he couldn't even get his Jeep out of his driveway. There he was in this little bungalow in the middle of India, indoors. So he began to pray, always a wise thing to do. He said, "Lord, you know that I love you and I wanted to serve you. I've come clear across the world. I've gone to the very ends of the world, and you know how talented I am, how many skills I can offer. I want you to use me mightily and greatly, and yet here I am in the middle of a monsoon rain. What can I do?"

The Lord spoke to him that day and said, "It's up to me how far you go and how high you go. It's up to you how deep you go." That's what He was teaching him that day.

The Johari Window

I discovered the Johari Window, which I want to share with you as a way to go deeper and also to know more about yourself maybe as a broken person, a person who can creatively suffer and can discover and help other people. It's a relatively simple psychological idea, but it's very apropos as a starting point for us.

THE JOHARI WINDOW

	Known to self	Not Known to Self
Known To Others	Open/Arena	Blind Spot
Not Known To Others	Hidden/Façade	Unknown

There are four squares. We can say first of all there are things that are known to self and known to others. That's our open, or public, self. We certainly know the public side of many of our celebrities, our politicians. There is a public self that we all have.

Then another box would be things that are unknown to self and known to others. That is called the blind self. There we don't see ourselves as others see us.

Next are things that are known only to ourselves about ourselves. No one else knows except us. We have a hidden self, and that would be a self that we know about but is unknown to others. We determine to keep it hidden. A minister who was being interviewed was asked, "What have you learned?" He said, "Well, I've learned one thing. There are some things that are between God and me, and that's where they're going to stay."

Finally we have the unknown self, and that would be the self that is unknown to ourselves and is unknown to others, but clearly that would be known to God.

How do we work this if we're trying to meditate on this? How do we go toward a deeper self? There are several dynamics. The first is discourse. We gradually share more of who we are with the people we can trust with that information. The public self moves more toward the hidden self. We ask other people to give us feedback about what they know about us. As they share, our blind self is more revealed to us. Disclosure and feedback, this is the stuff of therapy. Whenever I sit with a patient I say to them, "This is not going to work at all unless you trust me and I trust you. Whatever you tell me is in confidence. We need to be honest with each other." This is the beginning premise. So discourse and feedback would move us deeper. That's where the beauty of something like this shows us that it works. I'm sure that's why George Parkhurst wanted us to use CFO principles to run the psychiatric unit at the City of Faith. We used to say to patients when they would come to us that the persons that

God wanted to be here are here now. We never did get to a crucial number of patients to keep the hospital open. But the ones that God wanted to bring to us, He brought to us and made a way for them to get there. We were excited about that.

Then as the dynamics go, we expand into unknown areas. That would be the deeper self. Using this Johari Window is a wonderful counseling tool. First of all, it will build relationships. You can take this and say this is a format for what we're going to do and how we're going to talk. It gives permission to people to give you feedback. Most of us will not give feedback to someone unless they really ask us. We're in a culture where you just don't want to do that. You don't want to comment about a lot of things that you might know. It's good to give people permission. You'll build relationships. The sharing itself is satisfying. Sometimes we don't even know who we are until we try to describe ourselves to another person. That's a basic principle of counseling. If you ever have a problem, it's good to begin to talk about it. We don't understand ourselves until we explain ourselves to another person. I've learned after 24 years of marriage that we need to get a consensus before we move in any direction. We need to be able to share and to reach a consensus, and not make the decision unless we can. In that way we know ourselves, and we know that the other person knows us.

Health care revolution

I mentioned last night how much of what we are doing now in medicine is alternative medicine. Part of it I thank God for. People are interested in prayer and healing. That is definitely where we need to be in medicine. We probably did not have hospitals before Christ. If you go back in history and try to find the ancient ruins of hospitals, they probably didn't have them or anything that resembled them. Yet because of Christian compassion, we began to have religious orders that would then develop hospitals. So medicine and the development of medicine—we call Christ the Great Physician—has very much to do with a spiritual search and a search for wholeness. So when we speak of alternative medicine, I think *hoorah*! Forget about the scientific medicine—we need to go back to the alternative medicine. We need to reconsider Descartes's Dualism. In the 1600s, French philosopher René Descartes philosophized that we could separate the body and the soul. That served a purpose hundreds of years ago. It allowed the church not to interfere with the scientific exploration of the body. You could then study the circulation, and you could do autopsies, things the church would not allow. We discovered a lot about the science of the body.

But that part has neglected the spirit. Now we can bring them back together. So alternative medicine is in fact many people becoming interested in prayer in medicine. We are bringing the two streams of healing together. We're going to move them to one place. That's what alternative medicine is doing in part. People are very interested in the total person. In many things when God is speaking, I think He speaks to people in various professions in various ways, and then only later do they all know they were led by God. It comes together. We take the next step. We wake up at four o'clock and we respond at that moment, and at nine o'clock we discover that God already had something else in mind.

A lot of us are broken in various ways. I want to focus on the healing part, but I also want to point out that from a healthcare standpoint, from a doctor's standpoint, we are on the very edge of another healthcare revolution. We who are Christians are going to pray for the healing and are going to see the miracles like Jesus showed His disciples when He "went about … healing all manner of sickness and all manner of disease among the people" (Matthew 4:23 KJV). We had the first revolution in healthcare in the germ theory. When we finally understood that diseases were transmitted by germs, and that people had to wash their hands and we had to have antiseptic technique, we saved many lives. We don't have outbreaks of typhoid anymore. We don't have Typhoid Marys washing dishes in restaurants anymore, spreading typhoid through the general population. We understand germs.

That was the first revolution in healthcare. The second one for us is what we could call the antibiotic miracle drug. Through the Army Air Force, my father studied medicine at Northwestern in the early '40s. The Army Air Force was putting them through school rapidly because we were fighting the war in the Pacific. We needed to have doctors out on the field as quickly as we could. My father was in the service and learning medicine. He said there were only 35 medicines that were any good, such as morphine, insulin, sulfa drugs, penicillin. Every year I get a new edition of the *Physicians' Desk Reference.* I stopped counting a few years ago, but for demonstration purposes I went back and looked; there were 35,000 medicines that were deemed effective to treat what they said they treated. So we have gone through a second revolution in this generation. We have expanded the life of people. But we haven't come to wholeness by any means. So we're on the edge right now of a third revolution, and we will only get healthier if we can put into practice Biblical principles. When I was in medical school someone gave me a book called *None of These Diseases,* written by two doctors. The title is a line from the book of Exodus, and the book outlines Biblical principles to live by that will help prevent disease. For instance, there is the principle of forgiveness. How many diseases would we prevent if we only practiced forgiveness? Dr. Parkhurst used to love to say, "If you don't get bitter, you'll get through." People would get bound up with bitterness and it would make them sick, and sicker, and sicker.

Social readjustment scale

There is something called the social readjustment rating scale. I want to share this with you because you can use this as a road map for your life as you make decisions, as you think about what you're going to be doing next. Consider for yourself, because we can almost be sure that the body can only handle so much stress and then something is going to happen to the body. Maybe in making a decision we could say, "I'll pray about that," and then really pray about that and wait for the Lord. He would then give us the answer. I'm going to go through these with you in a little detail.

My wife is a very wise person. You can quote me on that if you see her. Before she would marry me, she said, "You have to go to a course called Basic Youth Conflicts." Bill Gothard was teaching it at that time. It was quite a phenomenon in the '70s. I went to the one in Dallas. They rented a coliseum, and it was filled with Christians learning these Biblical concepts for living. He was cautioning people on the importance of being on the cusp of this revolution, this healing revolution we are about to have. He gave this illustration: When he was a youth minister in Chicago, they were in need of a van. They didn't have the finances within the church to secure a van. But they decided that they would pray about it first. They said, "Lord, you have given us this youth ministry. You want us to be here. You know that we will be more effective if we have a van. So we are trusting in you. We are not going to go into debt; we're not going to go sign a note and buy a van. We're going to wait for you to supply the van." He said that within a very short time the phones began to ring at the church. He said before it was over they had five vans in their parking lot that people wanted to give them. They said, "The Lord told us we should give you this van. Would you use it?" He was teaching that as a principle.

A lot of what we get into trouble with are the stresses that we take on ourselves. We are rushing to take on things. Let me just walk through this a little bit, and then you again can reflect on some of these things and even take your own pulse, so to speak, check your own social readjustment rating scale and share with someone if you want to. This rating scale was developed by two doctors, Dr. Holmes and Dr. Rahe, who were doctors in the time of World War II. We were fighting the war in the Pacific, and we knew it was going to be a long war. When the soldiers left home, they were sometimes gone for 45 months in the jungles. We were fighting the war in the Pacific and wanted to only send healthy people out. Holmes and Rahe developed this rating scale for use by the military. The idea was that if you have too many stresses in your life, your physical health is going to suffer. You're going to get sick because the weakest link, the Achilles heel—it may be headaches, ulcers, GI distress—but something is going to give. Or something else is going to happen. You're going to start to have accidents. You're going to be distracted by your problems, you're not going to be thinking, you're not going to be effective. Or you will develop some type of mental disease. Depression, anxiety, even a schizophrenic illness, some major manifestation of mental illness can happen following periods of intense stress.

So they assigned stress points for different life events such as death of a loved one, divorce, career change, etc. Too many recent stress points, and you were out. One person in three was rejected, deemed unfit for military service and unable to go.

The Marines have told us at the VA that they train Marines as hard as they train anyone to fight battles. They train them to shoot on order, do anything on order. "Don't think for yourself, just obey." Yet when the battle begins, one-third of the soldiers will not fire their weapons, and those are well-trained soldiers who have made it through rigorous training. You can intend to do something but be distracted and not get it done, especially if you have too many other stresses.

Dr. Holmes and Dr. Rahe put out this scale and theory. It took millions of people taking this scale over a long period of time before official conclusions could be made. There were 16.6 million people who fought World War II, and then millions of people after that, up until 1967 when this was published. It looks like the human body is made so we can handle about 130 stress points. And then above that, you start to get ill in some way. When you get to about 160, 165 points, you often get major illness. I use this at work when people come in for psychiatric admission, and the average when they present to us is about 450 points.

Holmes and Rahe said that the most devastating thing that can happen to us is the death of a spouse. They said that's 100 points. You love someone, and you lose them. So right away the idea of being in mourning, going through deliberate mourning, grieving the loss for a year or two, is very important to do. That's enough, you have enough on your plate. You don't need to go out and do other things.

My father just passed away in May. The real estate agent is very wise and has been lifelong friends with our family. He said, "I've been in this business for years. If you can do this, this is the most healthy thing you can do: Don't sell the house, don't do anything for three years. Just sit on it, keep it up, do what you have to, but don't make all the major decisions right now. Wait three years." We know in psychiatry that we don't talk about grief being abnormal unless it goes past two years. Then we call it prolonged grief. We want people to work it out with their family, with their spouse, with their loved ones and with their church community. But this is going to change everything, the death of a spouse. So that's 100 points.

You can go right down the line. A divorce is 73 points. It's really rough on people. When you get married it's like two pieces of paper being pasted together. The paste dries; now try to take one piece of paper from the other. You can't do it without tearing both pieces of paper. That's what divorce is, two people have been one in God's eyes, now they cannot be split apart without tearing both lives up. Some of the good things that might happen can also be considered stressful: retirement, #10 on the list, is 45 points. Then we can go down to #37, a mortgage or loan less than $10,000. Some people have credit card balances more than that these days. That's a lot of stress. A man who has a car business in our town said that sometimes it doesn't seem that $10,000 is a lot of money. It doesn't buy very much. But try to pay it back, try to catch up.

Even the way we celebrate, like a vacation, is 13 points. Sometimes we overdo it. We have so many people come to the hospital at Christmas. They have just overdone it. In the mining business in West Virginia, the first two weeks of July, all the mines shut down. This was the tradition. All the doctors closed their offices. West Virginia closed up and everyone went to Myrtle Beach. This was in the old days when we had hundreds of thousands of miners in the state, and everything was built on this extraction industry. Everyone was shut down for two weeks. But that first week back was the highest rate of heart attacks that we had all year long. People hadn't slept right, they hadn't eaten right, they drank too much, then they try to come back and work and they have a heart attack. All of us doctors would have to take a vacation, and then when the miners got back we would have to work night and day to take care of heart attacks. That was a pattern that we saw. Even a vacation can be stressful. It can put people over the edge.

So use this as a guide, if you will, and then perhaps we can come to a point where we can be whole. The stress points are considered over the course of the previous 12 months. That's how you can use this as a road map. Measure yourself within the past year. Over time, you will have figured out a way to manage any stress so the pain and the burden of it lessens. What you want to do then, if you look at your life and you have just lost your spouse or just gone through a divorce, and you have some extra debt and you have this and you have that, this is when you want to turn to your friends and your church and say, "I really need your help for this year, particularly. I need to get through this year before I make other decisions. I don't want to go out of the frying pan and into the fire." But after a year, then you should be in a position to take on another stress and hopefully handle that.

Prescription for health

My father used to say no one would die of overwork when he was trying to get me to mow the yard or do some other chore. But they do die in Japan of overwork, of exhaustion. That is a disease in the Japanese culture. There was a large study done in New York State with resident physicians, who ordinarily would be healthy people. We take care of the sickest people in the hospitals. They would have doctors working 80 hours a week or more. So that would be 16-hour days. They determined by law in New York State that a resident doctor cannot work more than 80 hours per week.

It's important to set a prescription for your health to avoid overworking. There is a doctor named Dr. William Dement who is an expert on sleep research at Stanford University. He started his studies in the 1950s and determined that the human body is made to sleep ten hours a night. We think eight, and some people are proud that they can get away with six. But measuring longevity and function, the body works best with ten hours. So if you want to set out a prescription for health, plan to get ten hours of sleep a night for starters.

Dr. Kenneth Cooper from Texas pioneered the benefits of aerobic exercise. He developed exercise units, and we need a certain number of units a week. The body operates best if you can get the equivalent of walking three miles a day about five times a week. You don't have to do it every day, but we need that equivalency of aerobic exercise to operate well. Equivalencies could be things like biking, jumping rope, treadmill walking, etc. So if you put time into those two things—exercise and sleep—and also take off the Sabbath day, it would be virtually impossible to overwork.

Let me close with a Scripture which helps me in my grief and loss now as a wounded healer. It is God's promise from Isaiah 43:2-3,5 (NIV):

> Do not fear, for I have redeemed you;
>   I have summoned you by name; you are mine.
> When you pass through the waters,
>   I will be with you;
> and when you pass through the rivers,
>   they will not sweep over you.
> When you walk through the fire,
>   you will not be burned;
>   the flames will not set you ablaze.
>   …
> Do not be afraid, for I am with you;

God is good, all the time. All the time, God is good.

Camille Ashmar Almond, age 4

Camille Ashmar Almond, age 4

"The Bright Side"

Lecture by Rev. Paul L. Flanagan, circa 1920s

My grandfather, Rev. Paul L. Flanagan, served the Methodist Church in the mountains of West Virginia for over 50 years. He also suffered from tuberculosis and was healed from this disease. He prepared a lecture which he entitled "The Bright Side." This was back in the early 1920s when tuberculosis was a dreaded disease in West Virginia. With this talk he not only went from church to church spreading the good news of the Gospel and the healing power of Jesus, but he also went on radio and had a national message, which was practically unheard of at that time for a minister of any sort, much less one from Appalachia. Let me also hasten to say that he has had a profound influence on my life as my grandfather, the father to my mother, and I'm sure that my interest in ministry and healing took root in his life and the way he lived it.

****

"The Bright Side"
by Rev. Paul L. Flanagan

I want to ask for your patience while we go through the shadows for a little while. We shall then get into the sunshine where we will stay until the close. During the months when I was in our state tuberculosis sanatorium at Terra Alta, I found help in thinking these thoughts, and now I am happy in the privilege in giving them to others. My earnest hope and prayer is that through this message many may find a key to the bright side. I think I know something of the feeling of the one who said: "The inner side of every cloud is bright and shiny. I therefore turn my clouds out, and always wear them inside-out to show the lining." These familiar lines mean more to me since my sanatorium experience than ever before.

It was a typical winter day when I stepped out of Dr. Fulton's hospital in the city of Wheeling after an X-ray examination gave me the startling intelligence that I had tuberculosis. It was almost overwhelming, and I was shocked. The storm that was raging without on that blustery winter day was a summer's day compared with the storm that was raging within. I made my way to the home of my district superintendent, Dr. C.F. Anderson, and told him about my trouble. I don't see how anyone could have been sadder than I. As I sat in front of a window at Dr. Anderson's home, and with tear-dimmed eyes looked out at the blinding snowstorm, it seemed to me that the whole world had suddenly become dark. It was a day of shadows, a day of gloom.

What does it all mean? What will the outcome be? These were the thoughts that surged through my mind as with a heavy heart I took the streetcar to my home where I was the pastor. I hesitated to tell the members of my family but finally did so. "I must stop my work and go to our state tuberculosis sanatorium at once." These were the instructions.

It was some time before I recovered from the shock. But when I did, I began to pull myself together and began to think most seriously. What must I do? I realized that something must be done and done at once. I well knew that the gloomy and morose man is more likely prey for the tempter than the man of good cheer. It is in times of depression that this archenemy becomes unusually active. I also well knew that his most-used instrument was discouragement. The temptation to yield is terrible and supple. I did not feel that I was in any special danger at this point, but I said I must take no chances. I must lose no time in getting right into the game of getting well.

Now there were two sides of life at which I could have looked accordingly as I chose the bright side or the gloomy side. I could have been long-headed and wrong-hearted or the reverse, as I myself could determine. I had lost my health. Should I make matters worse by losing my head? Finally I said, "I'll take the bright side." I said it timidly, I know. My faith was weak, my courage still weaker. As if to encourage me in the stand that I had taken, the well-known lines came to my mind: "'Tis easy enough to be happy when life moves along like a song. But the man worthwhile is the man who can smile when everything goes dead wrong." I surely felt that things had gone dead wrong. But I had another feeling too. That was that perhaps I could get into the class of those who smiled as they passed through the shadows and even turned them into sunshine. And I thought, what a wonderful thing it would be if I could, like others whose patience and cheerfulness the world delights to recount, play the glad game along with the other game of getting well.

And since I have had the delightful experience of playing this glad game during those months of sanatorium life, I have a great desire to learn the game better and to play it more in the days that are ahead. I verily believe that all of us should have more moments in which we might be glad while counting out our mercies.

> All that we ever had could drive away the wrinkles
> and smooth the ruffled brow
> and soothe the heartaches
> from which we suffer now.
>
> 'Tis quite a game to play at,
> the ruse of being glad,
> in which we are the winners
> where prizes may be had.
>
> Glad games, were they played often,
> would so much sunshine bring,
> that all the bad
> would take to wing.

And is there aught a fireside
that this discontent reveals,
we hope that someone plays glad games
to oil domestic wheels.

Let's lift out tear-dimmed eyelids
so we can better see
our kind and heavenly Father
who hears our humblest plea.

To clouds grown dark with sorrow
and troubles soared aflight,
we hear if we but listen,
glad voices in the night.

When I decided to take the bright side, let come what may, it seemed that helpers appeared from every quarter. After I arrived at the sanatorium, I was given a paper to read by one of the nurses. It was *Outdoor Life*, and there were some things in it which would be of interest to me. I've almost forgotten now the things that I've read, except a little verse which seemed to be intended for me: "After the dark cloud passes, after the storm drops die, throw open wide your windows and smile up at the sky."

In a few days I received a letter on which by accident a drop of ink had fallen. By a few deft strokes of the pen, the writer had changed the blot into a pretty flower that really added to the beauty of the page. Something of the blot might have been scratched away with a pen knife. A rubber eraser might have removed a little more, but with the ink would have gone a part of the delicate paper. The eraser would have always remained to tell the story of the misfortune. But the figure into which the blot had been transformed made the page very beautiful. As I looked at that page, something seemed to say to me: "You may do this with the page from the book of your life, on which a blot of ink in the form of a bodily handicap has fallen. It need not be a barren waste, time irrevocably lost. Take the bright side, and you may transform it into something beautiful."

My church paper, the *Pittsburgh Christian Advocate*, soon began to visit me weekly in my new home. One day when the paper came, I went through it as usual. I don't remember now a single article in it but one. I do remember how Susan Hubbard Larkin just pointed her finger right at me and said:

> Those old blues are catching, don't you know? Let just one get them and they're sure to go. Clear through a family and when evenin's come, we're all a sittin' round so sour and glum, we can't see nothing good. That's what we do when those old blues once get a hold of you.

> There is something else that's catching. That's a smile that makes our troubles such a little, little pile. We feel ashamed to grumble and to fuss, when someone gives a loving smile to us. It sort of makes us happy through and through, that's what a sunny smile will always, always do.

> Let's catch the smiles then and drive out the blues. Inoculate against them and refuse to give them plans, because they always go clear through a family when one catches them you know. The rest will have them too, and when evenin's come, who wants to sit around so sour and glum?

Then there came to my mind to cheer and strengthen some noble examples of heroism and patience under suffering and disappointment. I thought of John Bunyan, whose body was a fettered captive but whose soul went on many a long and glorious quest. I thought of Robert Lewis

Stevenson, who also had tuberculosis and whose physical sufferings never dimmed that radiant light of cheerfulness which shines through all his letters. I could hear St. Paul say, "I have learned in whatsoever state I am, therewith to be content." And I could almost hear his song in his prison dungeon, as under pain and suffering. saying with as cheerful a heart and voice as when he was enjoying the hospitality of some loving friend.

A trio of helpers whose visits to the sanatorium always brought sunshine must not be overlooked. Dr. Aspinaugh, a fearless Bible storyteller; Dr. Bayless, the inimitable joy-lingerer; Mr. Taylor, the faithful Bible class teacher. Dr. Aspinaugh was pastor of the Methodist Church at Terra Alta. Dr. Bayless was pastor of the Episcopal Church in Oakland. Mr. Taylor was a member of the Terra Alta Methodist Church and had been at that time teaching the Bible class at the sanatorium for ten years. Rhoda Haber came to the rescue with his wonderful song "Carry Your Cross with a Smile." And someone, I don't remember who just now, cheered us with Alice Howthorne's "Whispering Hope." These were recordings. There were no radios. We had a phonograph in our cottage, a gift from someone. A number of other cottages were not so fortunate.

The optimistic farmer from across the hill brought cheer with his optimisms. Why? When wintering snows of February whitened the ground, he said no finer weather for the season could be found. It would help to make crops better, and every farmer should get lots of money to spend to make their business good. When winds of March began to blow, he said that April showers would follow shortly and produce the sweet May flowers. These would brighten up the year so that everybody's mind would be in a cheerful mood to pep them for the daily grind. Thus in every season, winter, spring and fall, he picked the bright and cloudy days as answering nature's call. And he reasoned in business to pick dollars from his plant, he must expect both light and gloom, so what's the use to rant?

Even Mrs. Riggs of the cabbage patch came and said, "The way to get cheerful is to smile when you feel bad. To think about somebody else's headache when yours is most busted. Get on believin' the sun is a shinin' when the clouds is thick enough to cut." Well, Mrs. Riggs's philosophy helped me. I'm glad she came. I want to recommend her philosophy to others, for I have really found that the best way to stop worrying over our own troubles, real or imaginary, is to look around us and find out how many people are worse off than we are. Then perhaps we shall feel that things are not as bad as we thought. Constant dwelling on our own troubles seems to magnify them. Every time we relate our woes, they seem more real to us. We should stop pitying ourselves so much, for self-pity is deadly. We should get out of our sack cloth and ashes, give ourselves a good scrubbing to get the ashes off and burn up the sack cloth. Then put on our finest raiment and sail forth like Solomon in all his glory. Life was meant to be joyous and glad. We were not meant to hang down either heads or lips. When we do, we only show we have departed from the path of true common sense as well as faith in God.

I want to say too that the courage and good cheer of a number of the patients with whom I was thrown daily was a wonderful stimulus to me. I could cite you many instances of this, but one will suffice. One man on our ward who had been getting along nicely for some months was taken down suddenly with pleurisy and high fever. For many weeks he was unable to go to his meals, and at last he began to improve. One day the doctor said, "You can start to your meals tomorrow." When he was getting ready to start along with the rest of us, I heard him humming a song. Then he sang the words softly. And what do you think it was? "He gives me joy in place of sorrow. He gives me love that casts out fear. He gives me sunshine for my shadows and beauty for ashes here."

I should be ungrateful if I failed to mention the smiling faces of the doctors and nurses and their many words of cheer and encouragement that helped create the proper mental attitude without which a cure would have been well nigh impossible.

I feel that right here I should say a few words in regard to the tuberculosis situation in our state and a word or two also to our state tuberculosis sanatorium. This institution has been doing a most wonderful work over the years. Our state had but the one tuberculosis sanatorium when I was there in 1923. There are others now. As we know, the newest is the old Sweet Springs Hotel in Monroe County. However, at the time I was there the southern counties thought it was too far. One poor fellow came 450 miles. Another said he would camp on the steps until they took him in. I wish that the people of our state would become better acquainted with the sanatorium as well as with our tuberculosis situation. The medical department consisted of the superintendent, three efficient and enthusiastic assistant physicians, and an ever-willing core of nurses who tended to the needs of some 200 patients in the eight cottages and the hospital. A splendid new hospital which takes care of 66 more patients was completed a few years ago. I have often wondered how the nurses could keep their smiles and their arduous duties with their many hours among disease and suffering. Where is there a class of individuals that is more self-sacrificing and doing more for the good of humanity than our faithful nurses? Dr. P.E. Clovis was the superintendent since the sanatorium was started in 1913. Through the commanding force of his personality, his innate ability and the unwearying application of his knowledge of men and medicine, he endeared himself to all those who were privileged to know him as physician and friend. Great as has been the organized crusade against tuberculosis, it is still a foe well worthy of increasing effective methods both in prevention and cure. The teacher in a certain school asked a boy to name the products of Argentina. The boy answered, "In Argentina, they have lots of tuberculosis, just lots of it."

"You don't mean tuberculosis, do you?" said the teacher.

"Well, that's just what my geography says," said the boy. "Here it is: 'They raise plenty of oil and wood for home consumption.'"

Now I don't know how much tuberculosis they have in Argentina, but I do know that they have lots of it in West Virginia. It is estimated in our state that 1 person out of every 100 has tuberculosis in a dangerous stage. One-third of all the deaths in our country between the ages of 15 and 50 are due to tuberculosis. And this is the age when the life of the individual is of the greatest economic value, and his death is the greatest loss to the community. Not counting the economic loss, think of the untold misery and suffering that these deaths leave in their wake. This loss can't be computed in dollars and cents.

There is a story about some shipwrecked sailors who drifted for days in a lifeboat down off the east coast of South America. Thirst had been chief among their sufferings, with no rain from which they might have obtained a few drops of fresh water. Their sea-bearing experience with ocean water had taught them that it was too salty for drinking. So they suffered and prayed and hoped for relief from a passing ship. At last in desperation one of the men scooped up some ocean water with his hand and drew it into his mouth. To his great surprise and joy, the water had no taste of salt and was drinkable. Their boat had drifted into the current of the great Amazon River which shoots far out into the Atlantic Ocean and for a length of several miles displaces the ocean water with the fresh water coming from the springs and brooks of the Andes Mountains. For days these men had suffered with thirst when all about them was an abundance of good water.

Such a story is not much different than one which might be written about tuberculosis and those who are temporally shipwrecked on life's sea by this form of illness. Really, for many who have tuberculosis, it is so easily obtained that oftentimes it is not recognized. If recovery depended on doing some big and spectacular task, many would spend every energy to the contest. But since success depends mostly on renunciation and apparently doing nothing, many are confounded and defeated by the very simplicity and tediousness of the task.

They are like Namen, the Syrian who said, "Are not the rivers of Damascus better than all the waters of Israel? Could I not have washed in them and been clean? Behold, I thought he would surely come out to me and stand and call upon the name of the Lord his God and wave his hand over the place and heal the leprosy." So he turned away in a rage, but his servants besought him saying, "If the prophet had bid thee do some great thing, wouldst thou not have done it? How much rather than, when he said to thee, wash and be clean?" (see 2 Kings 5:12-13).

The two most useful remedies in a cure—rest and outdoor air—are so commonplace that they are often overlooked upon only as of secondary importance. In some instances, golden opportunity is sacrificed by the tuberculosis individual who follows after some silly "-ism," wasting time and money in the expectation of physical benefit when the experience of thousands have shown that tuberculosis cures are affected most readily by the use of lung rest and outdoor air under a properly supervised routine. The 1922 death rate for tuberculosis in the United States was the lowest ever reported: 113.4 per 100,000. Still more striking is the fact that the tuberculosis death rate had been reduced by nearly one-half since 1911. This is an eloquent testimony to the labors of those who are devoting their lives to the cure of the disease. The body and the soul are so closely linked together in our present-day existence, that whatever helps the one helps the other. And whatever hurts the one hurts the other. We should always keep in mind that the work of the Lord Jesus during his brief ministry on earth was for the bodies as well as for the souls of men.

Well, I've mentioned some helps. You may be wondering if there were any hindrances. Yes, there were. Otherwise there would have been no fight at all. About the first jolt I received was when a man came to me when I was just getting my bearings and said, "A fellow came here some time ago looking a lot better than you did, and he was dead within a month." Well, that was some encouragement! About as much as the Irish Army Surgeon gave the wounded private. Said he, "Two of your wounds are fatal, but the third you need have no fear of. A month's good nursing will cure it." I must say I was just a bit fearful, being with so many persons who had tuberculosis, I might get it worse than I had it. But my fears were soon dispelled when I read that the sanatorium was the healthiest place in the country to live, as there all the laws of sanitation and hygiene are enforced. The difference between Hopemont, where the sanatorium is situated, and many other towns in our state is this: in Hopemont they know they have tuberculosis and are careful. In most every other town there are those who have tuberculosis and do not know they have it, and they are not careful.

Homesickness was another thing with which I knew I would have to contend. All my life I had been a home-lover. I would rather spend the evenings home with my family than to be any other place in the world. I never have liked my first school teacher. The very first day of school I was homesick, and he didn't sympathize with me a bit. When I thought of home and began to cry, he only looked at me coldly and said, "Paul, go out in the hall if you want to bawl." He thought he was smart in saying what he did, but he wasn't smart. It made light of a boy's feelings about home, and the boy never forgot it. Many nights when thinking of home and dear ones there, I would find comfort in repeating over and over again the familiar verse from one of our old hymns: "Peace, perfect peace, with loved ones far away, in Jesus' keeping we are safe and they."

There were two other things about which I was greatly concerned—eating and sleeping. I knew that if I didn't get the proper things to eat, and it may be that in the past I'd been accused of being a bit finicky along that line, I would get worse instead of better. About this time someone reminded me about what Methuselah ate. As I witnessed the numerous gastronomic feats in the dining hall, I soon decided to join in. The results were far beyond anything I had expected. For years I had tried every kind of food I knew about in order to gain weight, all to no avail, until at last I told my friends that I thought I was a hopeless case. But the tide turned, and I had a steady gain in weight the whole time I was there. I saw this bit of advice the other day in regard to eating. It's quite interesting, but I'm afraid it wouldn't do to follow it all the time:

Methuselah ate what he found on his plate,
    And never as people do now,
Did he note the amount of the caloric count.
    He ate it because it was chow.

He wasn't disturbed as at dinner he sat,
    Devouring a roast or a pie,
To think it was lacking in granular fat
    Or a couple of vitamins shy.

He carefully chewed every species of food,
    Unmindful of troubles or fears
Lest his health might be hurt by some fancy dessert,
    And he lived over 900 years.

I hadn't been sleeping well for several months, and I was just a bit fearful lest the coughing of the patients would keep me awake. The same day I got there a young fellow came in from somewhere in the Eastern Panhandle. I think that he must have coughed all night. But I said, if I am going to win this game, I must have sleep. So forgetting everything else, the soothing air of the mountains fanned me to sleep even amid the noises at times. I almost came to feel that that wonderful verse was descriptive of my own position: "The night shall be filled with music, and cares that infect the day shall fold their tents like Arabs as we silently steal away." The next place, I hadn't been used to sleeping on the outside. To begin that in late winter was a trial. One fellow who came shortly after I did inquired in all seriousness as to the direction of Pike's Peak. He was told it was on the mountain there somewhere. The hills about the sanatorium were snow-capped in the middle of May, and someone jokingly remarked that maybe the fellow was right. With these conditions prevailing, I also wanted to run to cover. For at first I must confess I hadn't much backbone. But I never voiced my fears to my cottage mates, for I would step out on the ward like a veteran and was soon buried in blankets with my feet resting against my warm and faithful friend, the pig. Conditions have changed somewhat since then. There is not as much sleeping on the outside to effect the cure, especially in the cold weather. Fresh air is obtained just the same. When I wrote home that I put a pig in my bed every night, my little six-year-old girl was puzzled. "Mother, does Daddy put a real pig in his bed?" For fear that there are a number here who do not know anything more about that pig than Martha did, I'd better tell you it was a contraption shaped like a pig that we filled with hot water and used to heat our beds. We could not have slept in the open without it.

These were some of the many things that seemed to stand in my way, but I'm glad to say that they were all overcome. It makes a great difference how you approach a difficulty. Obstacles are like wild animals—they are cowards, but they will bluff you if they can, if they see you are afraid of them. If you stand and hesitate, you take your eyes from them, they are liable to spring upon you. But if you do not flinch, if you look them squarely in the eye, they will slink out of sight. So do difficulties flee before absolute fearlessness, though they are very real and formidable, with vacillating contemplation.

Charlotte Perkins Gilman in her little poem "An Obstacle" describes a traveler struggling up a mountainside, bent on important business and carrying a heavy load. Suddenly a huge obstacle spread itself across his path. It did not move. He became angry and abused it. He knelt down and prayed it to let him pass. It remained immovable. Then the traveler sat down helpless before it, when a sudden inspiration seized him. He tells in his own words how he settled the matter:

> I took my hat, I took my stick,
> My load I settled fair,
> I approached that awful incubus
> With an absent-minded air --
> And I walked directly through him,
> As if he wasn't there!

Most of our obstacles would melt away if, instead of cowering before them, we should make up our minds to walk boldly through them. Well, when I began to wear a smile inside as well as outside, and may I say that the inside smile is just as important as the outside one, the whole place took on a different color. One fellow couldn't quite understand why I began the day in such a happy mood. He said to me, "You must be happy this morning." Maybe he thought it was a place where everybody was sad. I don't know. I answered, "Yes, sir. I'm always that way. There are lots of things to be happy about."

If we are cheerful and contented, all nature smiles with us. The air seems more balmy, the sky clearer. The ground has a brighter green. The trees have a richer foliage, the flowers a more fragrant smell. The birds sing more sweetly, and the sun, moon and stars appear more beautiful. My heart would thrill with joy at the gloriousness of every new day.

What a wonderful sight it is to watch the birth of a new day. To be in God's great out-of-doors and see the first faint dawn of the morning and watch the darkness scatter until the sun breaks forth in all his grandeur, radiant brightness and glory. It gave me a new sense of my Heavenly Father's world as I watched for the first green leaves of the woods, the spring grass and opening flowers. I learned a new lesson of confidence and trust as I looked at these things.

I remembered again the words of our divine Lord: "If then God so clothe the grass, which is today in the field, and tomorrow is cast into the oven; how much more will he clothe you, O ye of little faith?" *(Luke 12:28 KJV)*. When I noticed the first birds of springtime, I thought of our heavenly Father's care extended even unto them. I felt sure that if His eye is on the sparrow, I shall not be forgotten.

And at night, while looking up at the heavens above, I could hear the Psalmist say again and again, "When I consider thy heavens, the work of thy fingers, the moon and the stars, which thou hast ordained; What is man, that thou art mindful of him? and the son of man, that thou visitest him?" *(Psalm 8:3-4 KJV)*.

Bad old world? Well, I don't know. When I see the lilies grow, when I watch the roses bloom with their beauty and perfume, when at dawn I see the light rise triumphant from the night, when I note the golden yield of the autumn's harvest fields, when I hear the birds fly by, singing, whistling through the sky, when I hear a mother's song, this old world appears mighty good and sweet to me. He that has so many causes of joy in this old world is very much in love with sorrow and peevishness, he chooses to sit down upon his little handful of thorns. Could a better world have existed, God would have foreseen and created it.

After a number of months in bed, I was put on exercise and had the privilege of walking out for a while twice each day. My, what a treat it was. One day I noticed a very industrious bee. He did not seem to complain that there were so many poisonous flowers and thorny branches in his road. He kept buzzing on, selecting the honey where he could find it, and passing quietly by the place where it was not. There is enough in this world to complain about and find fault with if men have the disposition. We often travel on a hard and uneven road, but with a cheerful spirit and a heart to praise our Father for His mercies and blessings. We may like the bee keep so busy in extracting the sweet from all good things about us that we shall forget that there are thorns along the way. If we think thoughts about God and all the good things that He has made, our minds will not be troubled with gloomy forebodings. Let us not be grumblers and growlers at fortune, always finding that whatever is, is wrong, and doing nothing to set matters right, declaring all to be dark and gloomy, from Dan to Beersheba. I have learned this my friends, that I must be, and can be, satisfied and contented with other things and find my enjoyment in other things, if some former very great pleasures are denied.

****

Well, my friends, that is the lecture of Rev. Paul L. Flanagan, my grandfather, who had a very successful career in the ministry helping people not only with their souls, but also, as you can tell from this talk, to gain bodily health. I think that this is a capital illustration as how a Christian physician could also function. He could avoid using Scriptures in a mechanical, medicinal-dosage fashion, but rather apply them to life, finding the truth of God's Word in the out-of-doors, even in illness or hardship, in every facet of daily life. This type of analysis needs to be done continually by each of us who considers himself or herself to be in the healing profession. Of course I am grateful for my roots here in West Virginia and my roots in the ministry.

Let me lift up a final thought or two. Reverend Flanagan quotes from a song: "He gives me joy in place of sorrow. He gives me love that casts out fear. He gives me sunshine for my shadows and beauty for ashes here." Reverend Flanagan then goes on to mention how important the smiling faces of the doctors and nurses were. He also notes how much encouragement and cheer their words were to him in helping him create and sustain a proper mental attitude that would lead to health. He says that he could hear St. Paul say, "I have learned, in whatsoever state I am, therewith to be content" (Philippians 4:11). This same song he could hear coming from Paul in his prison dungeon, as under pain and suffering he sang with a cheerful heart and a voice as if he were enjoying the hospitality of a loving friend. Indeed, we always have a loving friend in Jesus Christ.

ALSO AVAILABLE

The Stories of a West Virginia Doctor
    Harold Almond, MD

Tender Loving Care: Stories of a West Virginia Doctor,
    Volume II
        Stories of Harold Almond, MD as told to
        Greenbrier Almond, MD

Stories of a West Virginia Doctor's Son
    Greenbrier Almond, MD

Stories of a West Virginia Doctor for His Grandchildren
    Greenbrier Almond, MD

Stories of a West Virginia Doctor for Kith and Kin
    Greenbrier Almond, MD

Stories of a West Virginia Family
        Greenbrier Almond, K Almond, Anne Almond,
        Ruthie Almond Wiewiora, Beth Almond Ford

More Stories of a West Virginia Doctor for Kith and Kin
    Greenbrier Almond, MD

God's Boot Camp
    Araceli Ganan Almond, MD

Available from:
        Artistry on Main
        27 E. Main St. Buckhannon, WV 26201
        304-460-2505

        McClain Printing Company
        1-800-654-7179 www.mcclainprinting.com

        Amazon.com